PROBLEMS AND TRENDS IN AMERICAN GEOGRAPHY

PROBLEMS and TRENDS in AMERICAN GEOGRAPHY

Edited by SAUL B. COHEN

BASIC BOOKS, Inc., Publishers
New York   *London*

170170

The Authors

LEWIS M. ALEXANDER is professor and chairman of the Department of Geography, University of Rhode Island. His major interests are in political geography, marine geography, and the geography of Europe.

ROBERT H. ALEXANDER is a geographer in the Geography Branch of the United States Office of Naval Research, Washington, D.C. His principal research interests are in natural resources and in new techniques for the collection and analysis of geographic information, including the use of airborne and spaceborne remote sensors.

JAMES M. BLAUT is visiting professor of geography at Clark University and was director of the Caribbean Research Institute, College of the Virgin Islands. His research has concerned itself with peasant agriculture in Southeast Asia, the Caribbean, and South America.

JOHN R. BORCHERT is professor of geography at the University of Minnesota and chairman designate of the Earth Sciences Division of the National Research Council. His research interests are in the application of geography to the problems of public policy and education and in regional planning.

SAUL B. COHEN is professor and director of the Graduate School of Geography at Clark University and a past executive officer of the Association of American Geographers. His research interests are in political geography and marketing geography.

NORTON S. GINSBURG is professor of geography at the University of Chicago and a past secretary of the Association of American Geographers. His research interests are primarily in the Far East on the one hand, and in political and urban geography on the other.

JEAN GOTTMANN is professor of the human and economic geography of the United States at the École Partique des Hautes

Études (Sorbonne) in Paris, and has been for twenty-five years on a transhumance between France and America. His main field of interest is economic and political geography.

JOHN FRASER HART is professor of geography at the University of Minnesota and a past executive officer of the Association of American Geographers. His research interests focus on the geography of rural people and landscapes in the United States.

PRESTON E. JAMES is Maxwell professor of geography and chairman of the Department of Geography, Syracuse University. His research interests are in the study of Latin America and in the history of geographic thought.

GEORGE KISH is professor of geography at the University of Michigan and chairman of the United States National Committee of the International Geographical Union. His research interests include geography of politics and of planning, Europe and the Soviet Union, and history of geography and cartography.

CLYDE F. KOHN is professor and chairman of the Department of Geography, University of Iowa, Iowa City, and president of the Association of American geographers. His research interests are in social geography, especially in the area of population and settlement geography and in the teaching of geography at all levels of instruction including the elementary and secondary schools.

WALTER M. KOLLMORGEN is chairman of the Department of Geography, University Distinguished Professor of Geography at the University of Kansas in Lawrence, and past president of the Association of American Geographers. His present interests are in agricultural geography, historical geography of the United States, and public policies and programs in resources development.

HAROLD M. MAYER is professor of geography at the University of Chicago and a member of the faculty committee of its Center for Urban Studies. He consults extensively in city planning and transportation to public and private organizations, and his research focuses on urban development and transportation.

ALLAN R. PRED is assistant professor of geography, University of

vi

California, Berkeley. His research interests are in developing models to serve as guidelines in the interpretation of the locational dynamics of economic phenomena.

GORDON E. RECKORD has just retired as assistant administrator for the Area Redevelopment Administration. He has served as executive secretary for the Chief of Secretariat of the Marshall Plan and as analyst for the Psychological Strategy Board of the Office of the President. He is currently doing consultant work in his area of interest, planning and developing of economic regions.

KIRK H. STONE is research professor of geography at the University of Georgia in Athens. His principal research interests have been in the process of new rural settling throughout the world, the morphology of rural settlement, and the geography of population. His principal field experience has been in the Northern Lands and is now being extended in the low latitudes and the Southern Hemisphere.

EDWARD J. TAAFFE is professor and chairman of the Department of Geography, The Ohio State University. His fields of interest are economic, urban, and transportation geography.

EDWARD L. ULLMAN is professor of geography at the University of Washington. From 1959 to 1961 he directed as visiting professor the Meramec River project at Washington University in St. Louis. During 1965 and 1966 he was president of the Washington Center for Metropolitan Studies. His research interests are in transportation and urban geography and in geographic theory.

GILBERT F. WHITE is professor of geography at the University of Chicago. His current research is centering on international river development and on human choice of different adjustments to water scarcity and abundance.

Preface

There is no problem in this world that is exclusively geographical; but there are few problems that are not in some way geographical. For the geographical or spatial is one of two dimensions—the other being time—within which physical and cultural processes forge our man-environment system.

The horizons of geography, historically, were limited only by the bounds of man's images of the world in which he lived or of the world in which others were presumed to live. Classical, medieval and scientifically enlightened geographers were cosmologists, prone to hypothesizing on the nature of the man-earth system. They were a pioneering breed of generalists, dedicated to science in its broadest philosophical sense. But the particularization of knowledge, which is characteristic of modern science, put a stigma upon the work of these generalists. Geographers, as well as others, began to adopt more specialized approaches and more rigorous techniques. This inevitably led to a narrowing of their outlooks.

In geography, man-land relations, areal variations, and distribution evolved as approaches using very specific techniques. These approaches all have had their champions in American geography, and they have contributed to a more sophisticated and scientific field. But in the retreat from cosmology, something was lost. The reluctance to generalize and hypothesize on great issues on a large scale became endemic, and while there have always been great figures in American geography who have not been loath to grapple with the search for universal truths, they have been rare.

A most significant and heartening development since World War II, and especially in the last decade, has been a reassertion of this earlier tradition in geography. The purpose of this volume is to express the concern of modern American geography with the significant issues of our times. Initially broadcast overseas as lectures for the "Forum" series of the Voice of America, the volume covers a variety of topics, related to both the United States and the world scene.

The fact that American geography today is problem-oriented is reflected in the themes of the individual authors. Geography has always focused on the real world. Current concerns therefore represent a strengthening of this tradition in the light of new analytical techniques and increased data. E. A. Ackerman sums it up thus: "Geography . . . contributes to treatment of the great problems of scholarship. This is a full understanding of the vast overriding system on the earth's surface comprised by man and the natural environment. Indeed, it is one of the four or five great overriding problems commanding the attention of all science" (E. A. Ackerman, ed., *The Science of Geography,* Washington, D.C.: National Academy of Science–National Research Council, 1965).

Certainly the approaches utilized by the authors reflect, or at least imply, a variety of methodological techniques. But as Preston E. James puts it in the first chapter of this volume, "the future of [geography] . . . requires . . . the integration of diverse ideas and approaches for the purpose of gaining greater and greater understanding of the complex interplay of elements in the earth's spatial systems." The empiric-inductive and the theoretical-deductive; the humanistic and the scientific; the field-cartographic and the mathematical; the descriptive and the predictive are all traditions that have strong voices in American geography, and the contributors are scholars who reflect these diverse traditions. But common to all is the concern for that which is spatially significant.

The oft-quoted adage that "geography is what geographers do" is valid only within a spatial context. Without it, there would be no discipline, no scholarly field. Thus, over and above the focus on current problems, there must be commitment to the study of the chronological.

The horizons of American geography are ever-widening. These essays are not an attempt to cover the entire field, but rather to indicate major directions and interests in current geographic thought.

This "Forum" series was sponsored by the Association of American Geographers. The editor is indebted to the Committee on Lectures of the Association, which aided in the selection of themes, topics, and contributors.

SAUL B. COHEN

Clark University
Worcester, Massachusetts
June 1967

Contents

PROBLEMS AND TRENDS IN AMERICAN GEOGRAPHY

1 CONTINUITY AND CHANGE IN AMERICAN GEOGRAPHIC THOUGHT

Preston E. James

Man has always felt himself to be associated with a particular place on the face of the earth. He has identified his tribe or his nation not only with the traditions and customs of his culture, but also with the hills and valleys and rivers and the distinctive plants and animals that together make up his homeland. In fact, place is a part of both the expression and the practice of culture. Man has always been concerned also with what lies beyond the horizon. He wants to know how the unknown resembles his home or how it differs. He wants to know whether the land on the other side of the hills is more fully endowed with resources to make life easier. Long before the dawn of written history there were individuals who were ready to explore unfamiliar places and to describe what they found there. But it was not until the second century before Christ that Eratosthenes first applied the word "geography" to this field of learning.

Finding and reporting on what makes one place different from another on the face of the earth requires certain skills—skills in observing and skills in expressing the observed. This is the verbal tradition in geography, which goes back to the ancient Greeks. Part of the process of analyzing place involves measurement. Geographers have always been concerned with the accurate measurement of distance and direction and the establishment of position on the surface of the earth. They have been concerned with

3

size and shape and height and depth. This is the mathematical tradition, which goes back at least to Thales of Miletus (640 B.C.). And, of course, geographic scholars are concerned with explana- tions of the interrelated phenomena which give distinctiveness to place. Since the time of the ancient Greeks, geographers, like other scholars, approached the search for understanding from two opposite points of view. Those who followed Plato felt that real- ity existed only in the mental images of phenomena and events. These were the theory builders, for whom observed phenomena and events were but the blurred shadow of reality. Those who followed Aristotle, on the other hand, felt that one should "go and see" and then build theory to account for what is observed. In geography there have always been followers of the theoretical- deductive method and followers of the empirical-inductive method.

Geographers who were curious about places on the face of the earth also found their work often in demand for practical pur- poses. What kinds of resources does a part of the earth offer? Are the conditions of soil and climate favorable for agriculture? What do we need to know about other groups of people for trade or conflict? These are practical questions, and geography has always had a strong tradition of practical utility.

There was a time when one scholar could master everything of importance about place. This was possible up to the tremendous elaboration of knowledge in the last century or so. Before the modern period geographers, who commanded unusual knowledge about the earth and its parts, enjoyed great prestige in the world of scholarship. But perhaps the last person whose knowledge of distant places was matched by his command of many different sciences was Alexander von Humboldt, the German geographer who died in 1859. This date marked the end of the period when any one scholar could presume to approach universal knowledge.

Even before the beginning of the nineteenth century, geo- graphic scholars were beginning to specialize. It was demon- strated that new understanding of the processes of change at work on the face of the earth could be gained by isolating each kind of process and examining it separately from other kinds of processes at particular times and in particular places—as a chemist can watch a chemical reaction in a test tube. Various substantive fields of learning appeared, each defined by the subject matter being examined. Students of such diverse processes as those of physics, or biology, or economics, or government remained separate, each subject developing its own vocabulary.

Today the separateness of the various substantive fields has been challenged. The most exciting advances in science have come from crossing the conventional boundaries between academic disciplines. The common form of communication, understood by workers in the most diverse fields, is the language of mathematics, and through mathematics each separate field of learning can contribute its bit to the total structure of man's knowledge. Geography is among those fields to which mathematical procedures have been widely applied since 1950.

Geography remains that field of study that focuses its attention on particular places on the earth's surface. Geographers look for those associations of phenomena and events of diverse origin that distinguish one segment of earth-space from others, or which tie different segments together in a functioning system of interrelated parts. The systems that occupy different parts of the earth's surface are made up of elements studied by the various substantive fields. The specialists in the study of a particular group of elements formed by a particular kind of process can describe what happens when a sequence of events is started and when "other things are equal"—in other words, when the process is isolated from the modifying effect of other things and processes. It is the geographer's special task to see what modifications of the ideal sequences of events are to be expected when "other things are not equal"—that is, in the total environments of particular places. Geographers now focus attention on spatial systems analysis, in which the elements of the system are of diverse origin.

All these changes in geographic purposes and methods have

been reflected in the evolution of geography in the United States. In the early period of the colonies, when all students in the colleges pursued the same courses of study, geography was one of these courses. It was offered in the junior year at Harvard in the late seventeenth and early eighteenth centuries. The text was the General Geography of Varenius, as revised and brought up to date by Isaac Newton. Students learned about the motions of the stars, the planets, and the moon. They learned how to fix the precise position of a place by latitude and longitude. They learned how scholars divided the surface of the earth into distinctive regions based on the associations and interconnections in area of plants, animals, and inanimate nature. They learned how to make and read maps. The first geographic text published in America was one by Jedidiah Morse in 1784: it was a universal geography, based on similar works published in Great Britain, all representing variations on the theme in the General Geography of Varenius. Morse's texts, frequently revised to keep up with the rapid pace of geographic discovery, dominated geography teaching in the colleges until the end of the first quarter of the nineteenth century. By that time a universal geography had ceased to be useful, even when it was expanded to several volumes. Geography, often described as "the mother of sciences," was replaced by the study of the separate substantive fields.

Interest in what is beyond the horizon was rekindled in America with the opening of the West. Lewis and Clark set imaginations afire with their exploration of the Missouri and Columbia drainage systems. After the Civil War, four separate surveys of the West were organized. Ferdinand V. Hayden started with the Nebraska Territory and then expanded his work westward to Colorado and to what is now the Yellowstone Park. Clarence King organized a survey along the fortieth parallel from the Sierra Nevada eastward to the Great Plains. Both these surveys were financed from Washington and were directed to make maps and prepare reports on the nature of the land and its resources. John Wesley Powell, who gained national attention by his exploration

6

of the Colorado River, later was supported by the Federal Government in his surveys of the West. His "Geographical and Geological Survey of the Rocky Mountain Region" had a strong utilitarian objective including the mapping of potential irrigation land. But the people who were interested in attracting new settlers were not at all interested in objective maps showing the actual areas where irrigation might be successful. Powell was instructed by the Congress to stick to geological work. His success in including surveys of other elements of the region, including the people, is a triumph of his administrative skill over Washington policies. Meanwhile, the fourth survey under the leadership of George M. Wheeler was directed to prepare topographic maps not only as a base for geological studies, but also showing mines, farms, villages, roads, railroads, and dams useful for the planning of economic development. In 1879, all these surveys were combined in the United States Geological Survey.

Later surveys of land and resources, each one more effective than its predecessors, include three: the Michigan Land Economic Survey of the 1920's and 1930's; the surveys of the Tennessee Valley Authority in the 1930's; and the Puerto Rico Rural Land Classification Program of the 1950's. These were inventories of land and resources as a basis for planning economic development. In 1965 this technique has been adopted in Latin America as part of the program of the Alliance for Progress. As time goes on, the methods of field observation have been improved. First came the use of vertical air photographs; now comes the use of "remote sensing" devices which promise further perfection of detail in mapping the phenomena that occur together on the face of the earth.

Geography began to reappear in college curricula during the last three decades of the nineteenth century. This was the "New Geography." Here is the way one author described his objectives:

Physical geography . . . is the science of the earth as a great individual organization. In this science the material body of the

7

globe, with its atmosphere, the myriads of plants and animal forms living upon it, and man himself, as a part of the life system, are not only considered in themselves, but in their mutual relations, as working together toward a common end. Though entirely resting upon the solid basis of observed phenomena, it does not stop there. Its aim is pre-eminently the discovery of the laws which govern these phenomena and of the grand chain of causes and effects which explains the mode of their occurrence.[1]

By changing a few words, and overlooking the teleological reference to common ends, this could be translated into spatial systems analysis. It was written by Professor Arnold H. Guyot of Princeton in 1873.

Geography, in American universities in the late nineteenth century, was in most cases taught by geologists with little or no training in geography. The physical and biotic features of the earth were treated with skill, but the economic, social, and political processes were described as responses to the so-called geographic environment. The acknowledged leader of the geographic profession in America before World War I was William Morris Davis of Harvard University. Davis, whose genetically conceived theoretical model of the sequence of events in the development of land forms was widely adopted both in America and Europe, recognized the need for a balanced treatment of both natural and cultural features. But his solution was to treat the cultural features as responses. This was the period of environmental determinism in America; these concepts dominated American geographical thought at the time when they had already been discarded in Europe. Geography then was distinctly an out-of-door subject, requiring field observation. Students were encouraged to formulate hypotheses and to test them against new observations. The writings of William Morris Davis contain numerous essays on how geographical studies should be organized

[1] A. H. Guyot, *Physical Geography* (New York: American Book Company, 1873), Preface.

and how geographical findings can most effectively be presented and taught.

It was Professor Carl O. Sauer, of the University of California at Berkeley, who in 1925 brought the newest German geographical ideas to American geographers. He made clear what the German and French scholars had been saying and writing since the 1890's, that the physical earth does not, in fact, determine the human response. Gradually the core concept of modern geography emerged: the significance to man of the physical and biotic features of his habitat is a function of the attitudes, objectives, and technical skills of man himself. This asserts that the determining factor in the man-land systems is the culture, or traditional ways of living, of the inhabitants. Natural resources, to be sure, are produced by physical or biotic processes, but they become resources, or cease to be resources, as a result of changes in man's attitudes and technology. A historical view of the changing significance of the resource base in any region demonstrates the inadequacy of the concepts of environmental determinism. Or put another way: with every change in the attitudes, objectives, or technical skills of a people, the meaning of the resource base must be reevaluated. Although a few teachers in American schools still teach environmental determinism, most of the professional geographers in America abandoned this theory many decades ago.

In 1938, Professor Richard Hartshorne, then of the University of Minnesota, was on leave from his university for a year of field study in Europe. Hartshorne was scheduled to carry on detailed studies of certain European political boundaries; but the year 1938 was not the best one in which to examine boundaries in the field with notebook and camera. Instead, Hartshorne spent his year's leave piecing together a report on the development of geographic thought through reading in European libraries and through visits with numerous European geographers. In 1939, he published his monumental work—"The Nature of Geography." The unfolding of geographic ideas from the ancient Greek times

9

to the present is described in "The Nature of Geography" in masterly fashion.

Hartshorne points out that the eighteenth-century German philosopher, Immanuel Kant, was perhaps the first scholar to formulate in words the distinctive position of geography among the various fields of learning. Kant, who lectured on physical geography at the University of Königsberg in the late eighteenth century, is reported in student notes to have started his course of lectures by outlining the three basic ways of organizing human knowledge. It is possible, Kant said, to focus attention on the study of a group of related processes, regardless of when or where the processes actually occur. Thus, in the laboratory the processes of physics, or chemistry, or biology can be studied in isolation. This is the *substantive* approach, and the one most familiar to us in the modern world. In modern academic organization, divisions and departments are defined in terms of the processes they study. But, as Kant pointed out, it is also possible to study sequences of events of diverse origin. This is the *chronological* approach, most commonly but not exclusively associated with history. And it is also possible to focus attention on the association and interconnections among diverse things and events that occur together in the same area. This is the *chorological* approach, most commonly but not exclusively associated with geography.

When Kant distinguished these three ways of organizing human knowledge, he was not offering a new idea concerning the relations of the fields of learning: rather, according to Hartshorne, he was only putting into specific words an idea commonly accepted among scholars. The German geographer, Alexander von Humboldt, made the same distinction, without quoting Kant. And in the late nineteenth century, another German geographer, Alfred Hettner, again made the same distinction. In 1958, Rudolf Carnap in his "Introduction to Symbolic Logic and Its Applications" again distinguished between scientific languages that refer to phenomena and events and those that refer to coordinates of time and space. This classification of the fields of learning, which assigns geography to the chorological approach, is what Carl Sauer referred to as a "naïvely-given sector of reality"— meaning that these three ways of organizing knowledge are so clear as to require no argument. Phenomena that are the result of the same kinds of processes, or sequences of events, regardless of time or place, can be examined together, in isolation from the disturbing effects of other kinds of processes occurring at the same times and places. Or the interconnections among different kinds of events arranged in specific sequences of time can be the focus of attention. Or, as geographers do, the various kinds of processes— physical, biotic, or cultural—can be examined in their interconnections within specific segments of earth space.

This view of the place of geography among the fields of learning is still valid. It explains why geographers are sometimes accused of "covering everything" and why geography is sometimes found among the natural sciences, sometimes among the social sciences—yet not clearly belonging in either one. Since the time of Humboldt, however, no single scholar could even pretend to "cover everything," any more than a single historian could embrace all of human history with equal competence. Individual geographers must specialize, either topically or regionally. Yet geography as a field of learning provides for a distinctive spatial, or chorological, organization of all the phenomena and events associated on the face of the earth. Its distinctive mission is to develop theory regarding space relations on the face of the earth and to describe the modifications of ideal sequences of events when these events occur in the presence of other kinds of events in the same area.

What kinds of studies do geographers actually undertake in America? What is it like on the "growing edges" of this field of learning in the 1960's? An *Ad Hoc* Committee on Geography, appointed by the National Academy of Sciences — National Research Council with Edward A. Ackerman as chairman,[2] identi-

2 The other members included Brian J. L. Berry, Reid A. Bryson, Saul B. Cohen, Edward J. Taaffe, William L. Thomas, Jr., and M. Gordon Wolman.

fied four major parts of the field in which geographic scholarship seems to offer highly promising potential. These are: (1) location theory; (2) physical geography; (3) cultural geography; and (4) political geography. The committee also pointed briefly to the importance of regional specialization. In any case, geographers are dealing with spatial systems, or bodies of separate elements so interconnected within segments of earth space that a change in any one element results in changes in all the others. Guyot said geography was concerned with the "earth as a great individual organization." [3] He was saying that there is only one complete system—the whole face of the earth, with its numerous interconnections among physical, biotic, and cultural processes. But scholars cannot grasp so complex a system as this and so must identify subsystems small enough to permit useful analysis. The distinctive kinds of subsystems that geographers investigate are those that are interconnected in area. Therefore, geography can be described as "spatial systems analysis."

The same dialogue between the theoretical-deductive approach and the empirical-inductive approach that was set forth by Plato and Aristotle is found running like a connecting thread through American geographical studies. Unfortunately, some devoted followers of the theoretical-deductive approach are less than patient with those who insist on the empirical observation of things on the face of the earth. The latter emphasize the tradition of field study in geography; the former emphasize the tradition of theory-building. Both are essential. The progress of geography, like the progress of any field of learning, requires close and receptive communication between the theorists and the direct observers.

During the past two decades the field of geography in America has been greatly stimulated by the application of mathematical technique. Hypotheses regarding interactions among diverse sequences of events can now be subjected to more rigorous testing. The search for statistical regularities brings to light complex in-

[3] Guyot, *op. cit.*

terconnections that could scarcely be identified through map analysis alone. The National Academy of Sciences' National Research Council report, entitled *The Science of Geography,* quotes William L. Garrison as follows: "The techniques that distinguish these modern students of geography from the more traditional ones include the use of inferential statistics, the use of modern mathematics, including linear algebra, the use of set theory and the theory of graphs, and the use of programming techniques and simulation procedures."

In the United States today, students of location theory especially, are making use of these mathematical techniques to develop models of spatial interconnections among things and events of diverse origin. They are developing theoretical structure to describe and measure accessibility, connectivity, dominance, and hierarchy, in addition to the location and geometry of the connections themselves. Rather than seeking to describe spatial systems as they may actually be observed, these theory builders describe what the spatial systems should be if the goals were x, and constraints on the achievement of these goals were y and z. The most efficient solution of such an equation provides a norm against which actual observed conditions can be measured.

These same mathematical methods can also be applied to the study of physical geography, cultural geography, or political geography. Groups of geographers in America are actually working in these parts of the field and making important progress, not only in theory building, but also in contributing to the solution of practical problems of public or business policy.

There remains, also, the geographic specialist who is almost wholly devoted to the empirical-inductive approach. Many of these are regional specialists. The regional specialist devotes a lifetime to the observation of the interplay of diverse processes in particular countries or specific culture regions. He becomes an expert in the interpretation of things and events in foreign countries. He is immersed in a foreign culture, mastering its language,

13

its music, its literature, its politics, as well as its problems of re-source conservation. Scholars who achieve this kind of competence are not common, but the demand for their services continues to grow.

Geography in America is alive and growing. Life and growth, as in any field, produce controversy and dispute. But the future of this field of study requires not the victory of one segment of the profession over the others, but rather the integration of diverse ideas and approaches for the purpose of gaining greater and greater understanding of the complex interplay of elements in the earth's spatial systems.

SUGGESTED READINGS

Ackerman, E. A. (ed.), *The Science of Geography*. Washington, D.C.: National Academy of Sciences–National Research Council, 1965.

Broek, J. O. M., *Geography: Its Scope and Spirit*. Columbus, Ohio: Social Science Seminar Series, 1965.

Haggett, P., *Locational Analysis in Human Geography*. New York: St. Martin's Press, 1965.

Hartshorne, R., *The Nature of Geography*. Lancaster, Pa.: Association of American Geographers, 1939.

Hartshorne, R., *Perspective on the Nature of Geography*. New York: Rand McNally, 1959.

James, P. E., and Jones, C. F. (eds.), *American Geography, Inventory and Prospect*. Syracuse, N. Y.: Syracuse University Press, 1954.

Leighly, J. B. (ed.), *Land and Life: A Selection from the Writings of Carl Ortwin Sauer*. Berkeley: University of California Press, 1963.

Wright, J. K., *Human Nature in Geography*. Cambridge, Mass.: Harvard University Press, 1966.

2 THE TRANSPORTATION NETWORK AND THE CHANGING AMERICAN LANDSCAPE

Edward J. Taaffe

Geographers have long held that the study of areas can be approached in one of two ways: the static and the kinetic. Halford MacKinder's use of the terms "man-settling" and "man-traveling" was an early recognition of this distinction. In American geography, the kinetic tradition—with emphasis upon the linkages between points and areas, often referred to as spatial interaction—has become just as great a subject of geographic interest since World War II as have the characteristics of the areas themselves. In any attempt to view the significance of landscape and change within the United States, spatial interaction represents more than a research point of view; it is a basic departure point for furthering understanding of the most fundamental man-land relationships within their areal context. One can therefore view such topics as America's geographic regions, the spatial aspects of urbanization, the changing significance of production regions, from the context of the pervasive role of transportation, or, more generally, circulation, in the United States. As transport technology changes, linkages between places change, and the characteristics of the places themselves begin to change.

The key to much of this change lies in the interplay between transportation and regional specialization. Improvement in transportation affords greater opportunity for regional specialization. As an illustration of this relation, we might consider two cities, A and B, which at first are entirely isolated from all other cities. Of necessity, there will be a wide range of subsistence activities carried on around each city regardless of natural resources. Even though vast portions of the area surrounding City A might have the best natural conditions in the world for the raising of wheat, the amount of land devoted to wheat will be restricted to the consumption needs of the inhabitants of City A. In City B, on the other hand, there might be the best possible land for fruit and vegetables yet the production of these crops will be limited by the fruit and vegetable needs of City B's inhabitants. As transportation improves and the two cities are connected, the first signs of regional specialization will appear. Wheat will expand around City A, the low-cost wheat producer. Fruit and vegetables will expand around City B, and the two cities will ship their surpluses to each other. Their production patterns will then be complementary. Wheat is produced more cheaply around A than B, so it is cheaper for B to pay transport costs on wheat from A than to raise wheat itself. If we were to improve the transport system further and connect both with a world port, C, there would be an even greater tendency for A to concentrate on its regional specialty (wheat) and for B to concentrate on fruit and vegetables in view of the possibility of serving world markets. The payments for the specialties could be used to purchase from low-cost producers those commodities formerly produced, albeit inefficiently, around Cities A and B. Thus, a further improvement in transportation, or lowering of transportation costs, would result in an intensification of specialized production in all points and areas concerned. This brings us to a simplified statement of the relation between production cost differentials between any two points and the cost of transportation. As long as transport costs are greater than the difference in production costs for a particular commodity, it is not profitable for the inefficient or high-cost producer to abandon production and have the commodity shipped in from the low-cost producer. As transport costs decrease, however, and become less than production cost differentials, trade does become profitable.

The history of United States transportation may be viewed as a progressive lowering of transport costs through improvement, innovation, and mass marketing and an accompanying increase in interdepenedence and regional specialization. This has not taken place evenly throughout the country, however. Each transport innovation has benefited some places more than others. Thus, the patterns of specialization have been constantly shifting and adjusting themselves to new patterns of absolute and comparative regional advantage.

United States transportation may be divided into four spacetime eras: Local; Trans-Appalachian; Railroad Dominance; and Competition. During the Era of Local Transportation, preceding the Erie Canal and the Trans-Appalachian railroads, transport costs were high and regional specialization was minimal. A network of canals east of the Appalachians provided minimal interconnection between the larger and medium-sized Eastern Seaboard cities. A diversified agriculture developed around these canals and was maintained in such areas as New England, despite poor soil and climatic conditions. In the better agricultural areas on the western side of the Appalachians, the local nature of the transportation network restricted the amount of specialization. Although much of the land north of the Ohio River was suitable for grain farming, the cost of shipping grain to Eastern Seaboard markets was prohibitively high. The lowest cost connection for such bulk commodities was via the Ohio River to the Mississippi, thence downstream to New Orleans, and by sailing vessels around the tip of Florida and north to Baltimore, Philadelphia, and New York. The National Road reached from Baltimore to Wheeling, West Virginia, by 1818, but it was too slow and costly to compete effectively with the Ohio River–Mississippi route.

The Western- or Trans-Appalachian Era began with the opening of the Erie Canal in 1825. Together with a few other partially canalized systems such as the Pennsylvania Public Works (1834), the Canal provided relatively low-cost transport between the Ohio Country and the East. The case of the New England farmer provides a dramatic illustration of the impact of such lowered transport costs on regional patterns. Suddenly, the New Englander had to face competition from fertile lands west of the Appalachians which had a far better resource base than New England for the production of agricultural staples. The cost of transportation was no longer high enough to keep these low-cost products out of New England markets. In the Ohio Country, the area in grain began to expand beyond local consumption needs; the grain area in New England began to contract as New England consumers found market prices of Western grain to be lower than those of New England grain at a comparable level of quality. Before long, agriculture in the Ohio Country had become noticeably more specialized on grain; and grain farming in New England was in a depressed condition. Ease of movement between the two regions was further increased just before the Civil War when eastern railroads began breaking through the Appalachians. Good agricultural areas no longer had to be adjacent to canals or navigable waterways in order to capitalize on their superior resources by producing for distant markets. This put further pressure on eastern farmers who began to move toward greater concentration on those agricultural commodities which were still costly or difficult to transport long distances, such as perishable vegetables or dairy products. In reverse fashion, eastern manufacturers were benefiting from more accessible western markets. Their goods were driving out many of the goods formerly produced by local handcraft industries west of the Appalachians. Thus, the great urban and manufacturing complex later to be identified as Megalopolis began taking form as most of that area began moving away from agriculture toward a specialization in manufacturing.

18

The period between the Civil War and World War II could be termed the Era of Railroad Dominance. Railroads dominated virtually all forms of transportation, long and short haul, passenger and freight, bulky goods and high-value goods. The canals fell into disuse and the road network was virtually nonexistent. Once the Civil War ended, rails spread rapidly westward from the Appalachians, forming a dense network in the Midwest and sending long tentacles across the northern, central, and southern parts of the United States to connect with a developing network on the Pacific Coast. The basic pattern had become established by the turn of the century and most of the country's populace had been provided with access to the rail network.

Certain significant changes in the country's spatial organization were reflected in this rail pattern. During the Era of Local Transportation, the Ohio and Mississippi rivers linked the Midwest with the South. When the Erie Canal was built, there was a surge of settlement along the northern shores of Lake Erie and a series of north-south canals such as the Ohio-Erie were built to connect the Ohio River settlements with the Great Lakes-Erie Canal system. As the railroad rose to prominence, however, the east-west components of the transport system came to dominate the north-south components. The Civil War severed many of the physical and organizational ties between the Midwest and the South. These ties were replaced by closer ties between the Midwest and the Eastern Seaboard. Chicago, the burgeoning rail center, replaced St. Louis, the river center, as the gateway from western farm lands to the emerging American Manufacturing Belt. The country's main street became the various Chicago–New York routes, with such powerful railroads as the New York Central, Pennsylvania, and Baltimore and Ohio operating over them. The extension of the western railroads to the Pacific Coast further emphasized the east-west grain of organization.

As the rail network expanded westward, certain patterns of specialization began to develop in areas far from eastern markets, aided by a conscious railroad policy of lowering long-haul rates relative to short-haul rates. Low promotional rates were set by the railroads on certain long-haul commodities in order to give agriculture a start in the new western area by keeping freight costs low enough to permit competition in eastern markets. The effects of these policies are nowhere more evident than in the case of California agriculture. Low promotional rates and active work on the part of the railroads with fruit-growing cooperatives triggered the rise of citrus-growing in California. The large-scale development of this specialized form of agriculture would not have been possible with purely local markets. The low rates, however, made California oranges competitive in eastern markets both with Florida oranges and as a substitute for other fruit products. Thus, the market had expanded enough for California farmers to operate at scales of production which permitted effective utilization of their splendid natural resources. The bewildering diversity of California's agriculture today still epitomizes the far-flung patterns of regional specialization associated with the low-cost, long-haul transportation developed in the Railroad Era and continuing to the present. Many fruit, vegetable, and nut specialties have 80 to 90 per cent of their production concentrated in California although their consumption is concentrated in the East. Low transport costs on many other long-haul commodities during the Railroad Era served to promote other regional specialization in parts of the West: as lumber in the Pacific Northwest, and mineral specialties in the Mountain States.

Just as the Era of Railroad Dominance saw the development of agriculture in the Midwest and West, so it saw the extension of manufacturing from its earliest area of concentration along the Eastern Seaboard westward to the Great Lakes. A pattern of interdependence among cities began developing, whereby cities would develop specialties in certain types of manufacturing and trade with other manufacturing cities. Chicago, for example, was able to produce agricultural machinery effectively for its large agricultural hinterland; Pittsburgh was able to bring in iron ore and coal cheaply and to provide low-cost finished steel to the growing manufacturing centers both east and west of it.

With this surge in the interdependence, efficiency, and overall growth of the large cities, came an accompanying spread of their influence over all parts of the country. The cities constituting the American Manufacturing Belt emerged as a particularly large and powerful group during the Era of Railroad Dominance. These cities were located within a roughly rectangular area bounded on the west by a line from Milwaukee and Chicago down to St. Louis; on the east, from southern New England down to Washington. This relatively small northeastern sector of the United States came to account for a remarkably high percentage of the population and manufacturing of the country. Chicago, New York, and such "main street cities" as Detroit, Cleveland, Pittsburgh, and Buffalo as well as the other older seaboard centers such as Boston, Philadelphia, Baltimore, and Washington epitomized this growing metropolitan dominance. Rail competition was particularly keen within the Belt, and freight rates were driven to levels lower than those of other territories, thereby increasing some of the competitive advantages of the Belt cities.

The present transportation period, from the end of World War I to the middle sixties, might be described as the Era of Transportation Competition. As transportation technology advanced, it became more diversified and other modes of transportation became competitive with the railroad. In the twenties, the truck and private auto became strong competitors. Truck transportation had its initial impact on the relatively high-priced, short haul of manufactured goods. The private auto took over most of the short-haul passenger traffic, virtually wiping out the short-haul electric inter-urban trains. Both truck and private auto continued their expansion in the thirties as the nation's woefully inadequate road system began slowly to improve. Inland waterways, deepened and improved by federal projects, became extremely competitive for hauling bulky goods both short and long distances between points accessible to a waterway. These competitive inroads upon the railroads continued and even intensified after World War II. The toll road movement, which had started before the war with the Pennsylvania Turnpike, gained momentum during the early postwar years, to be replaced in 1956 by a massive federal program for developing a nationwide network of high-speed, high-capacity expressways. Trucks became competitive with railroads for longer distances and for a wider range of commodities. Moreover, long- and medium-haul passenger traffic was lost to the airlines as the nation's travel habits underwent a fundamental change. The railroads themselves shared in the rapid technological advances in the form of improved and automated procedures for classification and traffic control. Although much of the passenger and short-haul freight traffic was gone, the railroads by the mid-sixties were providing fast, low-cost transportation for long- and medium-haul bulky products. Significant moves toward coordination among different forms of transport were also gaining momentum in the mid-sixties in the form of piggy-back, fishy-back, and containerization.

The net result of the explosion of transport technology and the rise of transportation competition during the last forty years has been the overall lowering of transport costs and the broadening of areas of high accessibility to national and regional markets. This, in turn, has increased interdependence among cities and regions in different parts of the country. Opportunities for regional specialization have expanded and ramified. Truck farmers around large Eastern cities face increased competition as early vegetables from the South and Southwest become easier to transport; this threatens to wipe out the classical rings of vegetable production surrounding these cities. Frozen fish from New England ports penetrate farther into interior markets providing severe competition to local fisheries. Milksheds around big cities expand and become overlapping and competitive. The ramifications of regional specialization have become more complex and subtle.

One conspicuous result of the effects of improved transportation on spatial interaction and specialization is the increasing dominance of the largest cities. As transport has improved, the largest cities have spread out both in size and influence. They perform many functions more efficiently than other cities due to internal economies of scale, clustering of complementary activities, available supplies of specialists, and a variety of other reasons. More effective linkages between cities will permit the largest cities to become more competitive with medium-size cities nearby. A large city will typically absorb some of the functions of the smaller nearby cities, thereby expanding its own markets, attracting more population, and accelerating its own growth.

The increasing dominance of the larger centers has been noticeable since the earliest transport era. Along the National Road, for example, forty miles represented a good day's journey. Clusters of hotels were, therefore, located in towns closely spaced along the road and along other local roads on both sides of the Appalachians. Today the spacing between large centers has increased markedly with the cumulation of transportation innovations, and many of the early towns have declined or vanished, their commercial centers, including the railroad station hotel, being mere whispers of the prosperous past that was theirs. In the regions surrounding large metropolitan centers, a hierarchical sequence of dominance exists. The hamlet has lost virtually all of its function and persists as a gas station-general store combination on medium-density highways. The village has lost functions to the town, the town to the city, and the metropolis has usurped many of the functions of the satellite cities surrounding it.

The spread of largest city dominance is also evident among the large cities themselves. An examination of air travel linkages among the one hundred leading air travel cities of the United

States shows that the nine largest cities accounted for the highest percentage of traffic of eighty-seven of them. New York alone was the leading air passenger generator at thirty-nine of the cities, extending its dominance through much of the American Manufacturing Belt and into the major cities of the Southeast. Los Angeles and San Francisco accounted for more air traffic in the zone between Denver and the Pacific Coast than did any other city. Chicago dominated a zone between New York and the California cities, and Dallas and Houston dominated the Southwest. There was also a pattern of subdominance in two other regions. Seattle was the leading air passenger generator for the Pacific Northwest and was, in turn, dominated by San Francisco; Atlanta dominated a number of medium-sized Southeastern cities but was, in turn, dominated by New York. An examination of figures over a time span of twenty years showed that the move from two-engine aircraft to four-engine to jet accompanied the greater tendency toward concentration on the larger centers.

Transportation improvement has also stimulated the physical expansion of cities. The urban by-pass or peripheral highways, such as Boston's famous route 128, which have been built around major cities have had a particularly strong impact. These highways attract industry which, in turn, generates a leapfrog pattern of people moving from the city out to the suburbs beyond the periphery. With employment available at the periphery, job commuting distance is no greater from the suburbs than it was from the less attractive inner city area. This has contributed to the coalescence of suburban areas around Eastern Seaboard cities to form Megalopolis.

Thus, in the present period of intense competition among a variety of effective forms of transportation, there are many effects on shifting geographic patterns just as there were in earlier eras of limited accessibility when activity was confined to a few narrow zones along rivers and near ports. Today, the patterns are intricately interwoven, but each shift in transport technology and each change in network arrangement changes an entire set of competitive strategies of cities and regions. The geographer is keenly interested in these dynamic patterns as expressions of the relation between transportation and regional specialization, and as a fundamental aspect of the geography of the United States.

SUGGESTED READINGS

Daggett, S., *Principles of Inland Transportation*. New York: Harper and Brothers, 1955.

Owen, W., *Cities in the Motor Age*. New York: Viking Press, 1959.

Taylor, G. R., and Neu, I. D., *The American Railroad Network, 1861–1890*. Cambridge, Mass.: Harvard University Press, 1956.

Ullman, E. L., *American Commodity Flow*. Seattle, Wash.: University of Washington Press, 1957.

3 INDUSTRIALIZATION AND URBANIZATION AS INTERACTING SPATIAL PROCESSES: EXAMPLES FROM THE AMERICAN EXPERIENCE*

Allan R. Pred

Traditional views of industrialization as an economic process have failed to provide a satisfactory basis for a theory of the spatial characteristics and consequences of industrialization. The geographer is primarily concerned with the spatial structure of the economy. The concept of industrialization and urbanization as interacting spatial processes combined with geographic interpretations of newer economic concepts offer the possibility for a multidimensional and genuinely geographic view of the economic landscape. Such a view can eventually lead to a full "geographic location theory," a theory that will move beyond description of the distributional characteristics of American industry into the realm of causation and explanation.

Industrial location theory has traditionally focused on the firm and individual establishments and therefore has been preoccupied with optimizing location, with minimizing transportation

* Substantial portions of this paper have already appeared in print in "Industrialization, Initial Advantage, and American Metropolitan Growth," *The Geographical Review*, LV, No. 2 (1965), 158–185. The ideas are pursued at greater length in the author's forthcoming book, *The Spatial Dynamics of U.S. Urban-Industrial Growth, 1800–1914: Interpretive and Theoretical Essays* (Cambridge, Mass: The M.I.T. Press, 1967).

costs, with maximizing profits. These pecuniary and utilitarian objectives are well suited to the contemporary entrepreneur, economist, or the city and regional planner, but they do not satisfy the geographer with his comprehensive approach to landscape. The spatial organization of manufacturing, particularly in the developed economies of Europe, North America, and Japan, is a product of one to two hundred years of economic development. During this time the emergence of concentrated large-scale manufacturing and the meteoric growth of multifunctional metropolises have been dynamically involuted and nearly always inseparable. Consequently, geographic interpretations of industrial concentration, urban-size growth, systems of cities, and the intra-urban location of manufacturing should not be fettered by the myopic assumptions and narrow horizons of Alfred Weber's classical location theory or its modern revisions. Instead, in seeking an understanding of industrialization and urbanization as interacting spatial processes, traditional location theory ought to be modified and combined with such concepts as the principle of circular and cumulative causation, the adaptive versus adoptive dichotomy of locational behavior, the converging and dovetailing character of technological innovations, and stage of transportation. Hopefully, the marriage of these time-worn and younger concepts will eventually yield us a "geographic location theory" rather than an "economic location theory." Such a geographic location theory can provide us with insights into the economic landscape and the spatial structure of the economy as it exists, in contrast to current theory which provides us with guidelines as to the ordering of the spatial structure of the economy.

In order to illustrate how a more profound understanding of the existing spatial structure of the economy may be gained by viewing industrialization and urbanization as interacting spatial processes and by employing theoretical concepts beyond what is usually considered as traditional economic location theory, a few arbitrarily selected examples will be introduced.

CIRCULAR AND CUMULATIVE CAUSATION

Ten metropolitan areas account for roughly 40 per cent of the United States industrial production capacity. This disproportionate concentration of manufacturing in the highest-order centers of the American system of cities had its roots in the half-century following the termination of the Civil War, when the national economy completed its transition from a commercial-mercantilistic underpinning to an industrial-capitalistic base, and when the top of the urban hierarchy became more and more characterized by industrial, multifunctional centers and less and less by cities dominated by mercantilistic wholesaling and trading functions. The cities which emerged to dominate the urban hierarchy fifty years ago continue to do so today. In recent years especially, tertiary activities have been more instrumental than manufacturing in perpetuating the growth of the nation's largest metropolises. Consequently, contemporary urban-industrial concentration can be partially interpreted through a model of circular and cumulative causation which describes urban-size growth for major American cities from roughly 1860 to 1910.

Imagine a mercantile city, with some small previously existing industrial functions, which is indiscriminantly located in space and not engaged in market area competition with other cities— although it does import some goods that are not locally produced. Assumption of these essentially isolated aspatial and monopolistic conditions permits concentration on the growth process itself. Such assumption avoids the related problem of the growth of some cities at the expense of others that the author has elaborated on elsewhere.[1]

Further, imagine the introduction of one or more large-scale

[1] A. R. Pred, "Industrialization, Initial Advantage, and American Metropolitan Growth," *The Geographical Review*, LV, No. 2 (1965), 158–185.

factories whose location may have been rationally or randomly determined. This event sooner or later evokes two circular chains of reaction.

New manufacturing functions, whether or not they primarily serve local markets, will have an initial multiplier effect. New local demands created by both the functions themselves and the purchasing power of the labor force will call into being a host of new business, service, trade, construction, professional, and miscellaneous white-collar jobs. The combined effect of new industrial employment and an initial multiplier effect will be a significant population increment and the probable attainment of one or more new local or regional industrial thresholds. These higher thresholds will be sufficient to support completely new manufacturing functions as well as additional plants or capacity in previously existing industrial categories. Once production facilities are constructed in accordance with the new threshold levels, a second round of growth is instituted. Eventually, still higher thresholds are achieved. Plant construction, in response to the most recent thresholds, again generates a multiplier effect and higher thresholds. The process continues in a circular and cumulative manner until interrupted or impeded, perhaps by major shift in industrial location owing to raw material or labor shortages.

A second circular sequence of reactions occurs at the same time and compounds and reinforces the effects of the first. This interrelated chain stems from the increasingly complex network of interpersonal communications and confrontations which devolves from an expanding population. The multiplication of interactions between the growing number of individuals engaged in the manufacturing and tertiary sectors enhances the possibilities of technological improvements and inventions; it enlarges the likelihood of the adoption of more efficient managerial and financial institutions; it increases the speed with which locally originating ideas are disseminated; and it eases the diffusion of skills and knowledge brought in by migrants from other areas. Although, as

Schumpeter would have it, inventions and ideas are not immediately implemented but await an imaginative or aggressive entrepreneur to exploit them, implementation will eventually occur. Once new factories are erected or old ones enlarged, employment and population increase, the web of interpersonal communications is again extended and densened, the chances for invention and innovation are further enhanced, and the circular process continues, perhaps at an accelerated pace, until diverted or hindered.

The myriad subtleties and intricacies relating to the individual components of this model cannot be introduced here, nor is it feasible to dwell on the empirical evidence existing to substantiate the model. It suffices to say that the circular and cumulative process of urban-size growth in the late nineteenth century was reinforced by immigration, natural population growth, real wage increases, accumulating external economies, the declining locational influence of primary raw materials, and the concurrent operation of adaptive and adoptive locational processes. At the same time, some cities grew more rapidly and at the expense of others because transport improvements and reduced per unit production costs worked to the benefit of a limited number of centers already producing efficiently; because other initial advantages in the guise of site and situation, relative accessibility, labor and capital availability, and factory immobility favored the growth of already identified commercial centers at the expense of other cities; and because the combination of movement and oligopolistic competition supported the tendency of manufacturing to concentrate in a relatively restricted number of cities.

THE ADAPTIVE VERSUS ADOPTIVE DICHOTOMY
OF LOCATIONAL BEHAVIOR

Acceptance of an adaptive-adoptive dichotomy of locational processes furthers comprehension of the interacting spatial processes of industrialization and urbanization. Two opposing viewpoints exist: one—the adaptive—maintains that economic activities rationally adapt themselves to the conditions of the society in which they exist, in which case industrial firms would rationally locate in cities because of the local market size or the availability of localization and urbanization economies. The other viewpoint —the adoptive—asserts that activities react to their environment in ignorance, with the "lucky ones" being adopted by the system. Put in another way, the adaptive-adoptive dichotomy represents a conflict between economically rational and purely random forces. Acknowledgment of the concurrent operation of both these processes permits the statement of a number of associated generalizations.

For example, the earlier described circular and cumulative process of urban-size growth could be perpetuated or accelerated by the appearance of new factories, with their attendant multiplier effects, even before requisite threshold levels had been attained or innovations had been proven economically sound. In turn, the long-term adoption or survival of some plants would be one key to the disparate industrial structures existing in metropolises of nearly equal size. Such plants might have been located initially by chance because of incomplete and imperfect knowledge, or had chosen a metropolitan environment in an effort to minimize uncertainty and risk regarding input availability. Finally, if it is realized that the most common sort of adaptive behavior is the imitation of observed patterns of success, it becomes even clearer why metropolises of similar rank in the urban hierarchy more often than not have dissimilar industrial characteristics. For urban industrial specialization is often partially the result of historically accumulated imitations of locally successful industries which are characteristically "footloose" or are locationally unaffected by local and regional market threshold considerations.

TECHNICAL CONVERGENCE AND DOVETAILING INNOVATIONS

Industrial technological changes since the mid-nineteenth century have usually been comprised of a dovetailing series of developments, of a complementary and mutually reinforcing sequence of events. This was particularly true in the period between the Civil War and World War I. Then technological progress was mostly the fruit of individual rather than corporate and institutionalized efforts; and industrialization was distinguished by the introduction of a relatively small number of broadly similar productive processes to a large number of industries. Furthermore, during the same period, invention and implementation of invention, or innovation, were preponderantly concentrated in those places where there was a demand for improvement and a knowledge of existing problems. In other words, innovation tended to take place where manufacturing was found, and urban-industrial success tended to breed further urban-industrial success; or, alternatively, the communication-innovation cycle of the proposed circular and cumulative process of urban-size growth was enhanced by the fact that many production techniques, with little or no adjustment, could be converted from the manufacture of one commodity to another. The chain of linked innovations is most vividly illustrated by the

Leland, Faulconer and Norton Company (later the Cadillac Automobile Company) of Detroit. Founded in 1890 as a producer of machine tools and special machinery, the company introduced machinery for producing bicycle gears during the brief heyday of the bicycle, switched to building gasoline engines for motor boats when the bicycle industry began to decline, and by 1902 had undertaken the production of automobile engines.[2]

This specific example also casts further light on the anchoring of "footloose" industries in large urban complexes, where they need not necessarily locate from a cost standpoint, and the consequent evolution of different industrial structures in metropolises of similar magnitude. In short, the manufacture of special machinery, machine tools, and other high-value per unit weight products is apt to flourish at the place of invention, regardless of location or size, and, because of the dovetailing quality of technological progress, an already industrialized city is the most probable initial location.

Lastly, the multiplicative aspect of technological development in the late nineteenth century led to a general increase in the specialization of manufacturing functions, which often dictated locational proximity of successive stages of production. Again, the eventual effect of these new linkages and new divisions of labor was to compel otherwise locationally independent industries to settle in existing centers and thereby stimulate metropolitan growth. In most instances, the more complicated linkages demanded by twentieth-century technology have only served to magnify and ossify already identified urban and industrial location patterns.

STAGE OF TRANSPORTATION

Existing literature has demonstrated that the interplay between stage of transportation and journey-to-work patterns is inseparable from the related questions of intra-urban industrial

2 N. Rosenburg, "Technological Change in the Machine Tool Industry, 1840–1910," *Journal of Economic History,* XXIII (1963), 422.

location and urban morphology. Within this framework the assumption has usually been that no far-reaching alterations in journey-to-work patterns and intra-urban industrial locations occurred until the railroad was superimposed on the urban landscape. However, evidence available for New York City in the early nineteenth century indicates that a transportation innovation as modest as the horse-drawn omnibus had significant ramifications for the spatial structure of the city—even though the omnibus could not make better than four miles per hour under the best traffic conditions.

Although private hackney coaches had been introduced in 1786, regular-service local passenger transportation service was nonexistent in New York City at the onset of the nineteenth century. In the absence of any cheap service on prescribed routes, it appears that a journey-to-work was highly exceptional among the industrial workers and handicraft artisans of Manhattan Island. Place-of-work was identical with, or in close proximity to, place-of-residence; and in virtually no instance were the two divorced by more than one mile. Moreover, among the extremely small number of presumably pedestrian commuters, approximately 65 per cent ventured less than a quarter-mile.

By 1840, when almost all of the city's 312,000 people were crammed within the limited area south of Fourteenth Street, the situation was somewhat different. Regularly scheduled horse-drawn transportation had been in operation since 1827, and the daily volume of omnibus traffic was in the vicinity of 30,000. While most laborers continued to walk to work, or to dwell in their place of work, the percentage of those commuting more substantial distances had increased significantly. Now, only about 25 per cent of those with a journey-to-work traveled less than a quarter of a mile, roughly another 25 per cent commuted more than one mile, and journeys in excess of two miles were not uncommon. With these changes the labor shed, or area from which an establishment could draw its working force, was enlarged and the intra-urban locational mobility of some manufactures was augmented. Specialized locations which afforded land-cost savings, communication economies, and interindustry linkages were now feasible, and those families who could best afford it moved from the Battery to the Washington Square area, which was then near the edge of the built-up area of the city. Recognition of these changes wrought by the inauguration of a new stage of transportation is crucial to an understanding of the subsequent industrial and residential patterns of the city.

CONCLUSION

It may well be that the countless interlocking pieces of the locational mosaic do not lend themselves to facile reassembly in verbal abstractions; but if geographers are to be concerned analytically with the existing spatial organization of the economy in its broadest manifestations, it becomes necessary for them to resort to high-order generalizations and theories. More specifically, a "geographic location theory" ought to be sought after—a theory that answers geographic questions, but, like the body of theory existing in any other field, one whose resources know no disciplinary boundaries. "Economic location theory," with its optimizing goals, can aid geographers but cannot supply totally satisfactory answers to their spatial questions. Likewise, the somewhat deficient solution of what might be impishly termed "stochastic determinism" can be only partially useful.

Of course, no panacea exists. But by interpreting industrialization and urbanization as interacting spatial processes and by utilizing concepts which have, to some degree, been previously alien to geographers, we can interpret the real, physically existent spatial structure of the economy with improved perception and focus. The concepts and examples presented in skeletal fashion here represent but a limited sample from among many alternative ways of thinking. We need not, for example, confine ourselves to delineating industrialization and urbanization as interacting spatial processes. We might instead consider all the geographic reflections of economic growth as interacting spatial processes. By so doing, the changing agricultural landscape would be incorporated into the scheme of generalizations. However, regardless of the approach chosen, the problem of developing geographic location theory remains one of being more precise and explicit in interpreting previous and ongoing empirical observations and field studies, and of synthesizing and conceptually embellishing these observations so as to identify those spatial processes which yield an ever dynamic, ever fluid geographic organization of economic activity.

SUGGESTED READINGS

Pred, A. R., "Industrialization, Initial Advantage, and American Metropolitan Growth." *The Geographical Review*, LV, No. 2 (1965), 158–185.

Pred, A. R., *The Spatial Dynamics of U.S. Urban-Industrial Growth, 1800–1914: Interpretive and Theoretical Essays.* Cambridge, Mass.: The M.I.T. Press, 1967.

4 URBANIZATION AND THE AMERICAN LANDSCAPE: THE CONCEPT OF MEGALOPOLIS

Jean Gottmann

Urbanization is an ancient process, gathering people in towns and cities. It has recently been greatly accelerated throughout the world, modifying the whole habitat of mankind. In this century, the trends of urbanization have taken on new and impressive forms in America. They are rapidly reshaping American landscapes and modes of life. Such have been the mass and speed of American urbanization, and so original many of its forms, that in many ways it announced, and in some cases determined, many of the characteristics of modern urbanization around the world.

Particularly interesting as a laboratory of present urban trends is a region stretching along the Northeastern Seaboard of the United States between the Atlantic Ocean and the Appalachian Mountains, from the general area of Boston to Washington, D.C., with New York City in its center. An almost continuous system of deeply interwoven urban and suburban areas occupies this region which had a total population of 37 million people in 1960. It straddles state boundaries, stretches across wide estuaries and bays, and encompasses many regional differences. This region reminds one of Aristotle's saying that such cities as Babylon had "the compass of a nation rather than of a city." To designate the region and the phenomenon, we proposed the name "Megalopolis" an ancient Greek word and also an old dream of building a very great city that would become central to the world of the time.

The term "Megalopolis" has been widely adopted since the book we so entitled was published in New York in 1961. Besides designating the region from Boston to Washington studied as a prototype of modern urbanization, Megalopolis has come to mean certain specific aspects in the present process of urban growth. There are at least three points to be carefully considered in the concept of Megalopolis. First, it offers the demonstration, on a huge scale, of the devouring power of large modern cities sprawling over the countryside around the old densely built-up nuclei. Second, such vast urban regions agglomerate a very large population: 37 million people living on some 53,000 square miles represent one fifth of the American nation crowded on 1.8 per cent only of the land of the conterminous United States. The average population density of the United States in 1960 was 50 to the square mile; in Megalopolis it reached 688. Thus, while the city seemed to scatter inside Megalopolis, this process represented a concentration of population on the national scale. Third, concentration developed also within Megalopolis as it contains five very large cities: New York, Philadelphia, Boston, Baltimore, and Washington, D.C., are metropolitan areas of more than 2 million people each. The central or downtown areas of these mighty cities may be emptied of population at nighttime, that is, of residential population as counted in the census, but they overflow with teeming crowds at noontime on working days. Last but not least, the concentrations of workers in the hubs of the large Megalopolitan cities do not consist chiefly of individual workers of the blue-collar type, but increasingly and already predominantly of white-collar workers occupied in offices, laboratories, and various trades and services. This has meant a considerable change in the appearance of the city, in its rhythms, functions, and in the mode of life of its populations.

The inner life of this vast urbanized region has come to be animated by a complicated crisscrossing of currents of dense traffic on the ground, on the waterways, and in the air. No other part of the world of similar size can offer a picture of as intensive movement throughout the area. In 1960, of the 37 million inhabitants, about 12 million lived in the five biggest cities within city limits; in addition, these cities daily received every morning a flowing tide, which ebbed back at night, of several million people. Besides, there were many trips between these major cities or between cities of smaller size, or even between suburban areas. An intricate network of highways, large and small, covers the whole area, constantly improving itself and becoming nevertheless increasingly inadequate for the ever-growing intensity of traffic by automobiles and trucks. The web of air lanes is almost as crowded, especially along the main axis of the region; for a number of years there have been several flights per hour leaving the New York City airports every day for Boston on one hand and Washington on the other. Since 1961 an air shuttle has been established among these three cities which the customer can board like a bus at the major airports. All this has been recognized, however, as already unsatisfactory, and a high-speed railroad is now being planned all along the 600-mile axis of Megalopolis, linking the major cities very much like a subway line inside one city. The flow of telephone calls and other messages between the different parts of Megalopolis is many times greater than what is observed between any other group of cities. All these currents of traffic illustrate the deep interrelations tying the various parts of the urban region together.

The land use in Megalopolis reflects the variety of the modes of life of its people and the powerful pull of the city. The whole area is far from being entirely covered with buildings as a city is supposed to be. In fact, about one half of the land area of Megalopolis is woodland. The percentage of the area under woods expanded even from 1946 to 1955, the decade of the greatest suburban sprawl devouring a very substantial acreage; but even more land previously tilled was abandoned by the farmers to natural tree growth than was consumed by urban and suburban uses. Some farming subsists within the urbanized region and in fact enjoys great prosperity. In as vast a country as the United States, with its well-organized system of transportation, agriculture could produce all the food needed by the urban population at some distance from the main concentrations. Only farms that could be termed suburban remain in Megalopolis; they chiefly specialize in the production of fresh milk and cream, poultry and eggs, fresh vegetables, and a few other special crops which can benefit by their proximity to a large consumer market. In central New Jersey, near the university town of Princeton, about halfway between New York and Philadelphia, a large dairy farm distributes the milk produced by a herd of almost 2,000 cows. The farm buildings look almost like a village, but there is surprisingly little acreage of green fields around it. Most of the food for the cows comes from far away; moreover, one sixth of the herd is always away, as the cows take a vacation two months a year on the green pastures of the Appalachian hills. These pastures are reserved for them by contract, and the cows are brought from the farm to the hills and back by a regular trucking service. These animals live the life of city folk, indeed. Similar stories would describe the raising of millions of poultry in many-storied buildings designed to house them. It is very intensive farming that goes on in Megalopolis; land and labor are too expensive in this area to allow for less; however, about 5 per cent in value of the total agricultural product sold in the United States is produced within Megalopolis.

This land use has come to be more and more regulated by public authority. The density of the population and the necessity to provide for the future require such regulation. More and more acreage goes into parks, land for schools, hospitals, highways, and other services to the community. Various kinds of zoning must be enforced, first in urban territory and then, increasingly, in rural areas. Much of the private land which still looks green already serves in practice, at least for part of the year, suburban purposes; for instance, the city dweller loves to go hunting or fishing not too far from his residence. Local or state authorities, of course, regulate this use of the land. Before such regulation was enforced, most wildlife of any interest to hunters or fishermen had practically disappeared from the woodlands and fields of this region; proper protection and regulation have now brought about a great abundance of deer; in places beavers have returned; and state services are regularly restocking the woods with birds and the rivers with fish.

The environment of Megalopolis may be termed completely artificial or man-made, even its greener parts. This is necessary to restore natural aspects and recreational quality to spaces despoiled, used, and re-used, by many generations of people increasing in numbers and density. There are still tens of thousands of square miles of beautiful open rural country, with mountains and rivers, lakes and seashores within Megalopolis close to the densely built-up urban areas. They must be organized and preserved to serve in adequate and multi-purpose fashion the needs of the local people. This is becoming an increasing concern of the authorities and of the citizenry.

Now, the properly urban uses of the land in Megalopolis may occupy only one fifth or so of the total area, but they are decisive for the whole system. This is where the actual densities of the urbanized region are pressing on the land, creating enormous needs and generating great wealth. Still, the majority of the inhabitants reside in buildings relatively spread out and many of them one-family detached structures, with some green around and between them. The population densities of the smaller cities and many of the suburbs are not very high compared to other urbanized regions around the world. In Northampton, Massachusetts, a town of about 30,000 people, the average density is about 860 per square mile, which is a little below the present density for the whole of the Netherlands (900), and much below the density of Hong Kong (8,700). In the larger cities, however, it reaches impressive figures: the average density for Washington, D.C., stood at 12,442 in 1960; in New York City it reached 24,700; and on the island of Manhattan, 77,200. These are figures of the residential, that is, nighttime population. In the middle of a work day the island of Manhattan harbors more than double its census population of 1.7 million, and the density on its 22 square miles reaches more than 160,000 per square mile. One may imagine the complexity of the task of servicing such a concentration of people and activities, the intricacy and magnitude of the equipment needed on the spot and around it.

The density of people and activities achieved in the main nuclei of Megalopolis has led, of course, to building in height and in depth, and to a strict system of interconnected regulations controlling the functioning of the whole system. The first high office towers, commonly called skyscrapers, were built in Chicago in the 1880's. But they really developed into a common device of urban architecture in New York City since 1900. Now the massive and lofty skyline of New York has become one of the wonders of the modern world. The skyline is scattering around, underlining the new role assumed in urban growth by offices and white-collar or nonmanual work.

It was quite natural for Megalopolis to lead the way in this urban style. This great concentration of people and economic activities, achieving early in its history a quite high average per capita income, was built on resources other than the region's natural endowment. Besides many good harbors and the deep penetration inland of easily navigable channels, there are few natural riches local to Megalopolis. There was, of course, abundant timber, some good soil, and in eastern Pennsylvania, a rich anthracite coal field. However, almost every region of the United States can boast more than that. The coal field nurtured some urban growth during the last century and attracted some industry, but it is today the most depressed part of Megalopolis, the only one that looks as if really declining. Its role in the Megalopolitan economy has always been minor. The cities of Megalopolis built their growth and prosperity on a kind of resourcefulness that had little to do with local natural resources. They started as hubs of sea trade and as a hinge articulating the web of maritime trade with the development of the continent. They used their brains, their skills, and hard work to achieve a rather phenomenal economic success.

As usual since the beginning of the Industrial Revolution in the eighteenth century, urban growth in Megalopolis developed in the fields of industry and commerce. In 1900, half of all manufacturing production in the United States was located within the present limits of Megalopolis. But now this region has only one quarter of the country's manufacturing capacity, and this proportion is bound to decline. In warehousing and wholesaling, while still very important, Megalopolis also sees its share steadily decreasing. Such trends do not mean necessarily a decline in absolute figures; one quarter of the total manufacturing production of the United States in 1960 amounts in volume and value, and even more in variety, to much more than one half of the American manufactures in 1900. But the trend in relative proportion is significant, because the greater part of industrial production and of the handling of bulky cargoes which used to be the duty and lifeblood of large urban centers, does not need any more to be agglomerated in such big concentrations. Factories and warehouses are leaving often the densely built-up parts of the city; they are moving out and sometimes migrating farther away out of Megalopolis.

Such a migration of industry does not entail necessarily a decrease in employment; it may mean only a shift in the categories of labor working and living in the cities and around them. In fact, the total manufacturing production in the United States employed approximately the same number of production workers (about 12.5 million) from 1950 to 1964, while the volume of the

43

manufacture increased at least 65 per cent. Similarly, employment in transportation and public utilities stayed during these same years at about 4 million, while the volume of these industries' turnover at least doubled. From 1950 to 1964 the total nonagricultural employment in the United States increased by about 13 million. This vast number of new jobs, equal to the total of the production workers in manufacturing, turned up in other sectors of the economy than industry properly speaking. Most of it came in such sectors as retail trade, finance, insurance, medical services, mass media, research, education, management, and government (particularly state and local government). These are now the fast-growing economic activities in the evolving American economy. This trend means more nonmanual, white-collar employment; and it also means that when industrial and warehousing plants leave the cities they modify the requirements of land use, the structure of the labor force, but it does not mean the ruin of the city. These trends, symbolized in the urban landscape by the rise of the skyline and by the urgent need for urban renewal over a large acreage in the heart of the old urban centers, should lead to a rebirth of urban civilization, molding new urban forms, in a cleaner environment, less polluted by industrial wastes, and for people less bent on hard physical labor but employed in occupations requiring them constantly to cultivate their skills and brains.

This trend is rooted in a very simple consequence of modern scientific and social evolution. What has happened to agriculture is now coming to manufacturing production: with increasing mechanization, rationalization, and other technological improvements of the production processes, labor's productivity is kept rising and unskilled labor is reduced to little use. The labor force first went from the farms to the cities; now, in the cities, the labor force must go to new and higher levels of employment. This has already happened for substantial numbers in Megalopolis; the 1960 census showed that in its population of 37 million, among the people aged 25 or more, 10 per cent had completed college or more. This proportion of adults with higher education is exceptional even in the well-educated Western countries and could not be found for any other area with a similar population size. The occupations and interests of such a labor force are reflected in some other statistics, such as the number of large libraries in the region: in 1957 there were in Megalopolis eighteen libraries with more than one million volumes each, and twenty-six libraries with one-half to one million volumes each; this density of large libraries is also unparalleled in any other area of similar size or similar population.

The economic evolution of Megalopolis is consistent with its historical past. These cities have always stressed the importance of commerce, information, education, and research. Today, the economic activities which are growing most rapidly—as measured by employment and payrolls—are deeply interrelated, and the hubs of a metropolis must accommodate next to one another the work places of such interdependent activities as commerce and finance, information and mass media, management of private and public affairs, research and higher education, specialized professional and consultative services of various kinds, adequate entertainment and recreational facilities, centers of art and culture. All the functions which the ancient city gathered in the Greek agora or the Roman forum, on the Acropolis and in the Academy, these functions are again becoming the backbone of urban concentration, while the industrial and warehousing plants are now allowed to disperse toward the smaller towns or even through rural territory, just like centers of agricultural production.

The concept of Megalopolis may therefore hold various indications as to the rapid and multifaceted changes now occurring in the American landscape. In many ways, the urbanized Northeastern seaboard, designated as Megalopolis, has served as the central laboratory of an experiment preparing a new order in the organization of inhabited space. The promise of the study of Megalopolis is exciting; but the present dynamic change which the region is undergoing cannot avoid creating some chaos too. The region and the interests at stake within it are so huge as to discourage clear and orderly planning of the whole evolution. Moreover, the promise of Megalopolis attracts many in search of opportunity, as large growing cities always have. Such cities normally offer great contrasts in the range of income, education, occupations, and origins of their inhabitants. These contrasts are bound to cause tension and problems. It has recently been estimated that of the labor force in New York City, while at least 10 per cent had higher education, about another 12 per cent were practically illiterate for all purposes of employment in the opening sectors of the economy. Also, the physical plant of the cities needs to catch up with the accelerated change and seldom succeeds. Chronic and acute problems of finance and government are bound to result.

The process of urbanization has not always helped to improve the landscape of the cities and of the countries where it has developed. Its recent acceleration has frightened many people and caused them to bemoan it. The study of Megalopolis shows urban growth trends offering the opportunity for improving the conditions of urban life.

SUGGESTED READINGS

Elias, C. E., Jr., Gillies, J., and Riemer, S. (eds.), *Metropolis: Values in Conflict.* Belmont, Calif.: Wadsworth Publishing Company, 1964.

Gottmann, J., *Megalopolis: The Urbanized Northeastern Seaboard of the United States.* New York: Twentieth Century Fund, 1961.

Gottmann, J., *Economics, Ethics and Esthetics in Modern Urbanization.* New York: Twentieth Century Fund, 1962.

Gottman, J., "Why the Skyscraper?" *The Geographical Review,* LVI, No. 2 (1966), 190–212.

Mayer, H., and Kohn, C. (eds.), *Readings in Urban Geography.* Chicago: University of Chicago Press, 1959.

5 SPATIAL CHANGE INSIDE THE AMERICAN CITY

Harold M. Mayer

American cities are undergoing rapid change, not only of their functions as centers of industry, trade, and innovation, but also of their internal structure. The changes reflect not only the changing nature of the urban functions but also are a cause and a result of the urban population's changing way of life.

Increasingly, the nature, extent, and patterns of change in cities and metropolitan areas are subject to control in the public interest; but the availability of such controls is subject to many constraints inherent in the democratic political process.

Although change in the urban structure is rapid, in any given period, such as a year or a decade, the existing inventory of buildings, utilities, and other physical plant within the city largely remains, and their replacement must be gradual. Thus, inertia plays a major role; and the city, at any point in time, more or less reflects the persistence of conditions more characteristic of the past than the present. The internal structure of most American cities, therefore, represents a combination of responses to past technology and conditions of life on the one hand and, on the other hand, contemporary conditions which include modification by the interposition of some public controls, such as zoning and subdivision regulations, building codes, and, in most cities, the development of comprehensive programs of planned public improvements. Increasingly, the availability of financial aid from federal and state governments has influenced the cities' internal structure, along with the operation of the market processes governing the choices of land uses. In recent decades, the population explosion and higher standards of living have together accelerated the expansion of the suburbanized areas: these are increasing much more rapidly than are the areas within the central cities of the metropolitan complexes and, in many instances, the older suburban municipalities as well. As a result the problems of urban and metropolitan government and planning are more complicated than ever.

The "overspill" is manifested in a proliferation of small municipalities with inadequate resources to finance and administer many of the urban functions on the one hand, and the growth of haphazard urban and suburban settlement in many areas entirely outside the jurisdiction of any local municipality on the other. This governmental fragmentation is especially troublesome in the larger metropolitan communities: the metropolitan area of Chicago has over 1,000 local governments, including some 400 municipalities and 600 special-purpose local governmental units, such as school districts, park districts, sanitary districts, forest preserve districts. The New York region has over 1,400 such local governments.

Local community interests and metropolitan interests operate at different spatial scales, and it is sometimes very difficult to ascertain which activities and which facilities should properly be of local, as distinguished from area-wide, concern. A major regional park and a local community park represent two different orders of magnitude, so does a neighborhood elementary school and a specialized high school or a university. The system of major expressways traversing a metropolitan area may be part of the federal interstate system, but it also furnishes much of the basic internal transportation of the metropolitan area. At the other end of the scale, the local access streets within a neighborhood represent a system of very different magnitude, yet both the expressway and the local street systems must be interrelated. A major airport serving the metropolitan area, and perhaps an extensive region beyond, exerts great influence upon the land uses in the communities for miles around it. The influx of underprivileged peoples into the older areas of a central city greatly affects the population growth of the outer suburbs, as peripheral movement of the metropolitan area's population takes place.

What, then, are the important recent and prospective changes in the spatial structure of American cities and metropolitan areas? There are three principal types of changes. These relate to land uses and functional areas, to transportation, and to population characteristics.

First, the areas occupied by urban development are expanding at an accelerating rate. The prospect is that the extent of the urbanized areas of the United States will continue to double every twenty years.

This reflects the rapid increase in urban population, the American tradition which aspires to a free-standing house on an ever-larger parcel of land, the virtually universal use of the automobile, and, of course, the rising standard of living which permits the luxury of ever-lower urban population densities.

The demand for urban land is increasing even faster than the increase in the urban population. In spite of the recent evidence of a trend in some of the larger cities toward luxury high-rise apartment living in the central areas, the prevailing movement of population is toward the periphery of cities, where space is available at relatively low land cost. In this way low densities become economically feasible for an increasing proportion of the population without the sacrifice of most urban services and amenities.

Within metropolitan areas, the deconcentration of the urban population is paralleled by a deconcentration of commercial and industrial facilities and activities. These activities generally produce lower intensities of land use than was true even a few years ago both because of the greater availability of land and the lesser number of persons served by each activity. The central business

49

districts of most cities have experienced a long-term decline in both relative and absolute importance in retail trade. Mercantile firms have established branches—in some instances as large as the original centrally located establishment—in the newer outlying shopping centers. These offer the inducements of adequate parking space and an attractive planned shopping environment as well as a location convenient to the residential areas. Such shopping centers require much more contiguous land than do the older types of shopping areas which typically consist of long ribbons of stores along one or more streets with little if any provision for off-street parking.

Similarly, industrial areas are deconcentrating. Lower densities produce less intensive demands on land in any one area, but a more widespread demand in general for land than was formerly the case. The comparative advantages of central-city locations for industry are challenged by the inducements of location near the fringes of the metropolitan areas and in some of the smaller towns beyond. Many industries no longer require locations along navigable waterways; bulk commodity transportation directly affects the locations only of large "heavy" industries, and water-borne package freight can be trucked to large-scale, efficient terminals— often in standardized containers without break-of-bulk and with consequent savings in handling costs. Many industries, also, have become less directly dependent on railroad transportation. Whereas a few decades ago the railroads handled as much as 80 per cent or more of the domestic ton-miles of freight transportation, they now handle less than half, even though their total volume has substantially increased. The motor truck is now responsible for over one-fourth of the intercity freight movement, and for an even higher proportion of packaged goods, including manufactures.

Furthermore, the advent, within the past decade, of integrated intermodal transport, using containers without break-of-bulk between origin and destination, offers the shipper the combination of the flexibility and lower terminal costs of motor truck pick-up and delivery, and the scale economies of large-scale, long-haul intercity transportation by railroad or water carrier. This has freed many types of industries from dependence on trackside or waterfront locations; they can develop locations without these former restrictions imposed by the older transportation technology. Most commonly, the modern Industrial Park has predominantly single-story buildings, with the advantages of straight-line production, and, in addition, ample off-street parking and centralized landscaping and service facilities.

Thus, a second noteworthy trend in the spatial characteristics of American cities is that residential, commercial, and industrial land uses are currently being developed at lower densities than in the past. This, combined with continuing rapid increases in the urban population, produces an ever-increasing demand for land to be urbanized. Urban agglomerations thus are spreading out rapidly. With inadequate public controls, the operation of the land-market mechanism produces what some people call the urban "sprawl" with mile upon mile of haphazard development. Tentacles of urbanization extend outward along the major transportation routes. In the late nineteenth and early twentieth centuries, these tentacles were oriented along the railroads with commuter service to the central city, and they were developed at relatively high densities. More recently, the newer tentacles, at somewhat lower densities, have as their main axes the highway routes, while the ubiquity of the automobile has produced a filling in, at moderate densities, of the former interstitial areas between the older radiating prongs or tentacles of urban settlement.

A third trend is toward the super-city, which results from the coalescence of adjacent metropolitan areas. Frequently, the radial tentacles of nearby cities spread toward each other, eventually coalescing into a continuous urban string, with a number of nodes, each represented by the core of a medium-to-large city. The largest of these string developments extends for 600 miles from north of Boston to south of Washington and embraces a population of about 40 million today (37 million in 1960). This agglomeration has been called "Megalopolis" and the term has come into widespread popular use. But there are many megalopolitan agglomerations: the Pittsburgh-Cleveland concentration, the area from north central Indiana to southeastern Wisconsin including Chicago and Milwaukee, the complex of metropolitan areas of southern California from Santa Barbara to San Diego, and so forth. The concept of the metropolitan area no longer represents the highest order of urban development; it is being superseded by this larger unit.

As cities spread out over extensive areas of countryside, the process of urbanization involves the conversion of ever more land from rural to urban uses, generally at lower average densities of population and structures than the land which was urbanized in the past. The typical profile of density, outward from the center of a city, involves a gradient with a pronounced peak in the center and with density decreasing, at an increasing rate, outward in every radial direction. This is true whether one is concerned with residential population density, height and density of buildings, volume and density of traffic generation, or land values. All of these are closely related. In the case of residential density in many of the larger cities, however, there is a crater in and near the center, where nonresidential developments occupy most of the land, leaving little available for residence, in spite of the recent pronounced trend toward luxury high-rise apartments in and adjacent to the central business districts of such cities as New York, Chicago, Philadelphia, and St. Louis.

Thus, the profile of a typical American city resembles that of a volcano even to the crater—in the case of residential and population density—in the middle. The lava flows are heaviest, forming ridges or spines, outward along the lines of most efficient transportation, whether rapid transit lines, suburban commuter railroads, or express highways.

As urbanization flows outward, embracing more and more land, there is a danger of inundation of all the scenic countryside and the immersion of all potential open space in the spreading urban mass. Recently, the federal government has provided for its increasing participation in the preservation of open space and the development of recreational and scenic amenities in the urban environment. No amount of interplay of the free market forces of supply and demand can provide for this open space; for the land values—and the concomitant policies of tax assessment—offer no incentives to the landowner to continue nonurban low-density land uses such as agriculture under the appreciation of land values which precedes the outward spread of the city and the demand for higher-density land development. A certain amount of control can be exercised through zoning, subdivision platting regulations, and other exercises of the so-called "police powers." Public intervention is essential to the preservation of the amenities of open space; these help give the urban structure a form and a cohesiveness which are, in some metropolitan areas, an outstanding feature of their internal structure. Fortunately, with all of its shortcomings, the "city beautiful" movement of the nineteenth and early twentieth centuries produced some of our outstanding parks and boulevards: Central Park in New York, the lakefront parks and a belt of large parks and connecting boulevards in Chicago, Golden Gate Park in San Francisco, among others.

All these spatial trends in American cities are interrelated, and an understanding of their mutual relationships is an indispensable prerequisite to any policies or actions that may be taken to affect the direction and nature of urban growth.

Several classical models of urban structure have been described. One is the concentric zonal hypothesis of the Chicago sociologists of the 1920's which views the city as a series of merging concentric circles, each consecutive outer circle being subjected to the "invasion" of a "succession" of land uses and population groups as the city spreads like waves from a stone thrown into a pool of water.

Another is the "wedge" or "sector" hypothesis which describes the city as a series of wedges, along which a given characteristic— whether it be a socioeconomic population group, a type of land use, or a cultural trait—will move outward in a straight line toward the periphery unless there are very strong counterforces, such as public intervention. A third is the multiple-nuclei hypothesis, which describes the city as a set of foci or nuclei around which particular land-use or population characteristics tend to group or stratify. Each of these hypotheses has a certain validity. Furthermore, they are mutually compatible, and each partially describes the typical city.

In the twentieth century, American cities have undergone an accelerating rate of change, reflecting increased mobility, principally as the result of the almost universal availability of the automobile which in turn is a reflection of a steadily rising standard of living. The automobile has been the principal catalyst in a significant number of major changes in the spatial patterns of American cities. It has blurred the clarity of the classical models of urban structure and growth; and while offering an increased number of alternative possibilities for new urban patterns, it has vastly complicated the choices involved in making locational decisions. It matters relatively little, if traffic moves freely, whether a given land use or establishment is located one or ten miles from those with which it maintains linkages; a family can have a much wider choice of residential location than in the days when the dominant source of employment was the central business district and access to it was completely dependent upon foot or animal transportation or public mass transit. Similarly, a commercial or industrial establishment is confronted with a set of possible locations within the metropolitan area; it need no longer be confined to the central part of the city.

Thus, a city represents a balance between two forces: centripetal and centrifugal, or centralizing and decentralizing. At any time their free operation is constrained by the inertia of patterns of land use, public and private capital plant investment, and habits, practices, and ways of thinking inherited from the past. Rarely do we have the opportunity to plan a city from the beginning, and when we do the city often outgrows its originally planned size, resulting in serious maladjustments of plant relative to contemporary needs.

Another way of looking at the modern American city is as a set of traffic-generating nodes and areas, interconnected by an internal circulatory system in the form of local streets, arterial streets, expressways or freeways and, in a few of the largest cities, by a system of mass transportation by rail, including elevated and subway lines and suburban commuter railroad services. Scores of comprehensive metropolitan transportation surveys have been made in the past two decades, covering most of the major metropolitan areas. They have developed plans for improving the circulatory systems of the areas with which they are concerned by considering, among other things, the traffic-generating potentialities of alternative patterns of future land use, and distribution of residential population in relation to commercial, industrial, recreational, and other nodal traffic-generating areas. Recently, such comprehensive planning of the interrelations of urban transportation and land use has been made a prerequisite to federal assistance to cities and metropolitan areas in urban renewal as well as transportation. As a result of these and other studies, several trends, already clearly evident in the recent past, may be projected into the future.

One trend, already mentioned, is toward lower average densities in the cities of the future. Cities are less crowded and more spread out. In many cities, such as Chicago, the peak traffic downtown occurred several years ago. Circumferential expressways bypassing traffic around the city centers, off-street parking facilities, changes in the functions of central business districts, and more efficient channelization and regulation of traffic have combined to produce more efficient patterns of circulation in the central areas

55

of many cities. But this has been at the expense of tremendous investments in expressways, and with difficult problems of relocating residents and businesses in their paths.

Urban land values reflect relative accessibility. Relative accessibility, in turn, represents a balance of two conditions: mutual proximity of interacting land uses on the one hand and transportation costs on the other. These two conditions represent simply another way of stating the balance between centrifugal and centripetal forces. One can pay a high price for central location in the form of high site rentals, high-rise buildings, and high traffic density on the one hand, with minimal transportation costs; or, on the other hand, at the price of higher transportation costs one can obtain lower densities, open space, relative freedom from congestion, and many amenities in the outer parts of the metropolitan area. The deconcentration of cities is not new, but the automobile has greatly facilitated it.

What is new, however, is the greatly increased area of accessibility; the interstitial locations between the earlier prongs of growth can be filled in at lower densities than were previously possible when all urban development was dependent upon public carriers, particularly rail. Not only has residential development decentralized, but the employment-creating establishments have, to a greater or lesser extent, also moved out from the central parts of cities and, in some instances, from the higher-density, rail-oriented suburbs as well.

The result of these changes in the urban pattern—as well as a cause—is a change in the pattern of circulation. A decrease in the proportion of the trips within urban areas, and in many cities an absolute decrease in the number of trips to and from the major nuclei, including the central business district, has taken place. Previously, the pattern of trips was essentially a radial one, with the major focus downtown; more recently, the radial pattern has been partially supplanted by a more diffuse pattern, with an increasing proportion of trips between origins and destinations other than the central business district.

This is an inevitable concomitant of the diffusion of homes, employment, and recreation, from the older core areas of the cities. It means that fewer people and jobs are within easy access of the public mass transportation lines. Fewer trips can effectively utilize the railroads, subways, and elevated lines, or even the busses which have supplanted the street railways. The result has been a substantial decline in the use of public mass transportation facilities in cities. These facilities can no longer operate economically since they are essentially adapted to carrying large volumes of travel at high densities.

Rail rapid transit facilities, in particular, are very efficient carriers of large numbers of people to and from origins and destinations which are heavy traffic generators. However, their efficiency applies only at those times when they can transport people during peak hours to and from the central business districts of the larger cities. Few cities have potential traffic volumes which would make substantial investments in these facilities economical, even with extensive provision for the use of lower-cost feeder services in outlying areas. During most of the day, the investment in right-of-way, equipment, and man power to operate these systems would be idle.

The average person commuting to work in the city, furthermore, owns an automobile, whether or not he uses it to get to work; but once he has made the investment in his car it is most economical for him to make maximum use of it. The governing consideration in choice of mode of transportation to work, therefore, is the marginal or out-of-pocket cost of the trip—including cost of time saved by the flexible door-to-door transportation provided by the automobile—rather than the fully-distributed cost spread over the total number of trips. Under these conditions, if an efficient internal circulation system by road can be provided, reaching all parts of the urbanized area and providing adequate parking at the concentrated destination areas, it would not be economical to provide a radial mass transit system in addition. Such investment, which must be of public funds, would be justified only by an explicit policy of subsidy to the central business district to enable it to compete on somewhat more even terms with the rapidly growing outlying commercial developments of the metropolitan areas.

The same forces of centralization and decentralization which condition the physical and functional patterns of cities are basic to many of the social and human problems which constitute major issues in urban areas. It has long been recognized that socioeconomic stratification exists in cities, that there is a high correlation between socioeconomic status and recency of arrival in the city, and that there are spatial patterns by which areas of social and economic homogeneity and heterogeneity can be identified. In other words, segregation, whether voluntary or involuntary, involves localization within the city by its very nature. Urban geography, therefore, must be concerned with the patterns of social, economic, and ethnic segregation which exist, which have developed in the past, and which are likely to persist or change, as the case may be, in the future with or without the intervention of public policies.

Cities have always attracted those people who were ambitious and who desired to take advantage of the wide range of economic, social, and other opportunities. In the United States, as elsewhere, immigration has always been the major source of urban population increase, although in recent years net reproduction has surpassed immigration. The immigrants, originally predominantly from abroad, initially settled for the most part in the older parts of cities which, naturally, were centrally located. As they improved their status they moved outward, sometimes maintaining clusters of social and national homogeneity, sometimes assimilating, more or less rapidly, into the general population; although for some groups certain constraints in the form of ethnic and national prejudices, buttressed until the Supreme Court decision of 1948 by ethnically restrictive covenants, slowed up the processes of areal mobility and social and economic assimilation.

In recent decades, the major sources of urban immigrants have been within the United States: the rural South, the economically depressed Appalachian areas, and Puerto Rico. The largest immigrant group, particularly in northern cities, has been the Negro. The Negro has at last achieved legal equality with other Americans although, unfortunately, the mores and prejudices against him in many areas persist. His opportunities to break out of the city areas to which he has traditionally been confined are less than those of the earlier foreign-born immigrants. The result has been the creation and persistence of Negro ghettos in many cities. Since, by both continued immigration and a higher net reproduction rate than that for the general urban population, the Negro population in many cities has been increasing rapidly, these ghetto areas are no longer sufficient to contain it, even at ever-increasing densities and accompanying pathological social and physical conditions.

The Negro ghetto areas have been expanding very rapidly, but in many instances not as rapidly as has the Negro population. The constraints against expansion have been wilfully maintained by many property owners for slums are profitable to their owners. Since most urban Negroes have been the unfortunate victims of centuries of discrimination, their educational level, hence their ability to overcome the limitations of their segregation in ghettos has been less than that of the groups which preceded them in many such areas. Where expansion of the Negro ghettos has occurred, it has usually been into contiguous areas previously occupied by people of somewhat higher socioeconomic status. These, in turn, have moved farther outward, often to the suburbs. Rare, indeed, is the urban neighborhood contiguous to an expanding Negro-occupied area which has successfully achieved real integration of Negro and white residents.

Furthermore, as the available supply of housing filtered down to the newcomers with less economic ability to pay rentals than that of the preceding groups, overcrowding and the accom-

59

panying pathological conditions are the inevitable results. Seemingly, the only way to counterdirect this process is through a concerted effort by urban renewal, including both land clearance and rebuilding as well as conservation and rehabilitation on the part of public authorities in partnership with private investors. In the long run, the improving status of the Negro resulting from equalization of educational opportunities will reduce the spatial differences of racial occupancy among the parts of cities and metropolitan areas, just as improved transportation resulting from the automobile is decreasing accessibility differences. But in the short run, the patterns of racial segregation, in spite of the trend toward "open occupancy," produce some of our most urgent urban problems, and they have significant spatial implications.

One of the most urgent problems arising from spatial segregation of the races within cities focuses upon the schools. This, in turn, arises from residential homogeneity. Residential homogeneity, in turn, is reflected in what planners have called the "neighborhood unit concept" although they never intended to imply that the neighborhood unit should be used as an instrument of segregation. The neighborhood unit, in turn, is related to the neighborhood school, which has been the focus of much of the racial unrest in New York, Chicago, Milwaukee, Boston, and other large cities.

Formerly, when the Negro population was small and the area of Negro occupancy was limited, it was possible to operate neighborhood schools which were racially integrated. For even though the areas were racially segregated, the district accessible to the neighborhood school, in which all parts were within walking distance for the children, could be defined so that it included predominantly white as well as predominantly nonwhite parts. As the Negro-occupied area expanded beyond that which could be included within walking distance of the neighborhood school, the school, of course, soon became all-Negro. School segregation is thus a reflection of residential segregation.

Because of disparities in the cultural environments of whites and non-whites, springing from long-time differences inherited from the past, the Negro children characteristically required compensatory educational advantages. These were not usually available in the predominantly Negro schools, for the more experienced teachers, who would be best equipped to provide them, sought assignments in schools serving those neighborhoods of higher social and economic status, where many of the classroom problems characteristic of areas of recent immigrants would not exist. The seniority systems of many cities permitted such teachers to avoid assignments in the predominantly Negro schools, in spite of the fact that they would be best equipped to deal with their problems. The Supreme Court, in setting aside the "separate but equal" doctrine, accentuated the problem; for the schools in the areas of recent, predominantly Negro, immigration are not only separate, but usually not equal, in spite of attempts in some cities to make them so.

If the school is to be the heart of the neighborhood unit, and the neighborhood unit is not integrated racially, then it follows that the school cannot be integrated. Many attempts to reorganize the spatial patterns of school attendance have been made in cities: transporting students to integrated schools outside of their own neighborhoods at considerable cost in time, inconvenience, and disruption of childhood associations; and clustering of schools in order to obtain a wider service area and thus a less homogeneous population. Both methods represent attempts to overcome the limitations of the neighborhood unit.

The neighborhood unit school is but one of the many spatial aspects of the urban population pattern. The more assimilated a population group becomes, the more closely will its spatial pattern of location within the city and metropolitan area resemble that of the total population. There will always be some people who want to be near others who share their common interests, origins, religions, and other characteristics. In recent years,

61

many writers have pointed out that in a large city, with our present mobility, it is not necessary, or even particularly desirable, to maintain physical proximity in order to achieve contact through mutual interests. Homogeneous suburban communities, it is pointed out, regardless of socioeconomic status, may not be desirable because the children in school are deprived of the opportunity to become familiar with children from groups unlike their own, and because the intellectual sterility of a homogeneous social environment creates a dull, monotonous life for the adults. City-wide, metropolitan-wide, and even world-wide communities of interest can, among the more fortunate economically and socially, substitute for propinquity.

Upward social and economic mobility may result in increased physical mobility. This, in turn, can produce a more homogeneous environment throughout the urban area. As this assimilation takes place, in the long run, the social, economic, and physical differences among the component neighborhoods and communities of the metropolitan area will become less significant, and each portion of the urban complex will become internally more heterogeneous.

A set of problems of increasing concern to urban geographers, sociologists, planners, school administrators, and others relates to the nature of the "grain," so to speak, of the city. Does the neighborhood unit, and the community of propinquity, have any reality in the long run? Should they? If they should and could, what should be their optimum population size? What kind of "mix," if any, of population groups would be desirable in each instance? How can a desirable mix be facilitated? What is the socioeconomic threshold for the achievement of the kind of physical mobility that can break down patterns of spatial segregation? These are essentially spatial problems, and therefore they are of interest to the urban geographer. But the geographer cannot solve them alone. They involve value judgments, and in their solution the geographer must participate with colleagues from many academic and applied fields.

SUGGESTED READINGS

Blumenfeld, H., "The Modern Metropolis," *Cities.* New York: Alfred A. Knopf, 1965, 40–57.

Chapin, F. S., Jr., *Urban Land Use Planning,* Urbana, Ill.: University of Illinois Press, 1965.

Harris, C. D., and Ullman, E. L., "The Nature of Cities." *Annals of the American Academy of Political and Social Science,* CCXLII (November 1945), 7–17. Reprinted in H. M. Mayer and C. F. Kohn (eds.), *Readings in Urban Geography.* Chicago: University of Chicago Press, 1959, 277–286.

Mayer, H. M., "A Survey of Urban Geography," Chapter 3 of P. M., Hauser and L. F. Schnore (eds.), *The Study of Urbanization.* New York: John Wiley & Sons, 1965, 81–113.

Murphy, R. E., *The American City: An Urban Geography.* New York: McGraw-Hill Book Company, 1966.

6 THE CHANGING AMERICAN COUNTRYSIDE

John Fraser Hart

Revisiting a familiar rural area in the United States one is impressed anew by a paradox: the countryside is filling up. To say that the countryside is becoming emptier is to say that many of the old familiar features of the farming landscape have disappeared or are disappearing. This may result from technological change which makes them obsolete, or from farm consolidation which makes them surplus, or from land abandonment which makes them derelict.

To say that the countryside is filling up is to say that many highways in rural areas are beginning to look almost like city streets. Hordes of onetime city dwellers have been moving to the country. In the ten years between 1950 and 1960 more than 9 million people, roughly one of every twenty Americans, moved to new homes in rural areas. The land along many paved highways is fast filling up with new nonfarm houses and commercial establishments. This is especially true along the highways within commuting distance of metropolitan areas, and normal commuting distances have increased extravagantly in recent years. Fifty miles or more is no longer an unusually long journey to work for the nonfarm people who live in the new houses along the highways; they can cover the distance in an hour or so.

The automobile, which has divorced the worker's residence from his workbench, and permits him to live where he pleases, has also divorced many countrymen from their plows and tractors and allows them to seek jobs in distant cities. The onetime farmer, who still lives some distance from the main highway, may travel to work in a car pool with four or five of his neighbors. Each drives his own car from his home to the highway, parks it there for the day, and then they all get into a single car for the long journey to work. Along many highways it is quite usual during the working hours to see clusters of automobiles parked at each road intersection.

What has happened to the land which once was farmed by the owners of these cars? In some instances, especially in rougher, hilly areas in the eastern half of the nation, it has simply been abandoned and allowed to grow up in weeds, briers, and brush. In some instances, it is still being farmed but only in a casual, part-time manner. And in other instances, it has been consolidated, either by rent or by purchase, with other farm land in the vicinity.

Farm land abandonment has been mentioned first because it is this recent change in the rural landscape which most startles modern Americans. As a nation, we are still accustomed to thinking of our land in terms of clearance, not of abandonment. One of our folk heroes is still the hardy pioneer who felled the forest with his trusty axe and brought the land into cultivation. It comes as something of a shock to many Americans, therefore, when they learn that more than 60 million acres of farm land, an area almost half the size of France, has been abandoned for farming in this country within the last fifteen years!

Through much of the eastern half of the United States, land which is not regularly mowed or cultivated will revert to woodland in half a century or less. This is precisely what has happened in a broad belt of country reaching from central Alabama northeastward to Maine. The spine of this belt of farm land abandonment is the rugged hills and mountains of Appalachia and New England. Although there are some exceptional areas, within most of this belt the acreage of open farm land has declined by a third to a half within the last fifty years, and much of this former farm land is reverting to woodland.

Many factors, in addition to job opportunities in nearby cities, have contributed to farm land abandonment. In the eastern hills, perhaps the most important are the steepness of the land and the replacement of horses by tractors. A team of horses can pull a plow or a mowing machine across a hillside which is too steep to be traversed in safety by a tractor. As a general rule, if a farmer cannot drive his tractor safely across a field, the field will soon revert to woodland because the farmer can no longer mow or cultivate it.

What has happened to the millions of acres that are no longer used for farming? In a distressingly high proportion of areas the answer, unfortunately, is nothing. Although much of the abandoned farm land in the eastern part of the nation has reverted to woodland, for the most part it is woodland of rather poor quality. Some wooded areas are carefully managed for sustained yields of forest products, but notions of efficient forest management are still quite alien to many rural landowners. On the positive side, however, if these areas of abandoned farm land are properly managed, they can become valuable forest areas. Of even greater importance, they must be thought of as actual or potential recreational reserves for the nation's growing urban population which is sure to need ever larger picnic grounds, parks, camp grounds, and hunting and fishing areas.

Turning now to the other side of the coin, despite the amount of land which has been lost from farming, agricultural production in the United States has been increasing rapidly in recent years. In 1790, for example, some 19 American farmers were needed to feed one single city person, but today the average American farmer feeds more than 30 city dwellers. In 1965, one man-hour of farm labor produced more than five times as much food as it did in 1920. In the two decades since World War II, agricultural output in the United States has risen by nearly one third.

The reasons for this increase might be labeled mechanical, chemical, biological, and managerial. Mechanically, horses have been replaced by machinery, and the old horse barn is rapidly disappearing from the American landscape. the modern American farmer needs two tractors: one to pull his machinery and equipment, and a second to serve as mobile power unit.

Chemically, he needs herbicides to control weeds and pesticides to control insects. His notions about the maintenance of soil fertility have changed dramatically. He has abandoned the old traditional crop rotations, he practices minimum tillage, and derives much of the productivity of his soil from a fertilizer sack. In 1945, American farmers used less than 3 million tons of chemical fertilizers (in available plant nutrients); by 1965, they were using more than 10 million tons!

Biologically, improvements in plants and animals have contributed greatly to increased agricultural production. The story of hybrid corn is an oft-told tale, but plant and animal breeders have made many other less heralded breakthroughs. Often mechanical, chemical, and biological advances have been interdependent. In southeastern Texas, for example, the introduction of a new rice variety, coupled with the development of a new chemical weed killer to control grass in the rice fields, raised the per acre rice yield from 3,100 pounds to 4,500 pounds in the four years between 1961 and 1964. While our engineers have been designing new machines to pick our tomatoes, our biologists have been designing new varieties of tomatoes which are easier for the machines to pick.

Turning to the managerial level, many farms have become increasingly specialized and have concentrated their efforts on intensive production of a few items to which their resources are especially well adapted. One of the more spectacular examples of agricultural specialization and intensification is the dry lot for cattle. A dry lot is nothing more than an enclosure which contains troughs from which cattle can be fed. The dry lots of irrigated areas in the West tend to specialize in fattening beef cattle. The largest beef cattle dry lots, although they cover only a few score areas of ground, may contain ten thousand or more beef cattle at any given moment. Food is placed in the troughs completely by machine, and a single worker can tend to the feeding of an astonishing number of animals in a remarkably short time.

Dairy cattle are more common than beef cattle on dry lots near cities in the West and in the urban Northeast. *The New York Times* recently described a dairy farm in Brooklyn which provides an extreme example of a dry lot operation. The farmer keeps sixty cows in a garage-like shed on only half an acre of land. He has a tiny exercise plot for his cattle, but they spend most of their time in the shed. Like many other dairy farmers in the Northeast, he grows none of the feed his cattle eat but buys alfalfa hay from the Corn Belt, citrus pulp from Florida, sugar beet pulp from Minnesota, and any other feed which he can purchase cheaply.

Even in the dairy country of Wisconsin, where farmers have traditionally turned their cattle out to pasture during the warmer months, the use of dry lot feeding is on the increase, and many fences have been pulled down because they are no longer needed. The farmers have learned that they can make the most efficient use of their pasture land by harvesting the forage plants when they are mature, and storing them as hay or silage until the cattle need them. This system, known as "green chopping," insures that the forage plants will be harvested at the optimum time and prevents loss of pasture by trampling and soiling.

Perhaps specialized agricultural management reaches its extreme in poultry production and in the citrus groves of Florida, but in two quite different ways. Most poultry production in the United States is now "vertically integrated." The poultry farmer provides buildings and labor, but the company which supplies him with chicks and feed also maintains complete management control. The farmer receives day-old baby chicks, which he feeds, waters, and markets as he is directed to do by the feed company. Although he receives a guaranteed price for the poultry he delivers to market, which protects him against the wildly fluctuating price of poultry, the farmer is not allowed to make any management decisions. Many poultry farmers feel as though they are paid laborers on the very land they own.

The management system in the citrus groves of Florida is completely different, for here the man who owns the land may never have set foot on it. He may entrust his grove to a production company which tends the grove and picks and markets the fruit. The cost of each operation is charged against his account, and these charges are levied against the profits when the fruit is sold. The grove owner may have no contact whatsoever with his grove other than the annual check which might be likened to a corporation dividend check.

The improved agricultural techniques, mechanical, chemical, biological, and managerial, which have increased production on a decreasing acreage of farm land have also enabled a single farmer to operate a much larger acreage than he could handle in the past, and demands for additional farm land exist in many parts of the United States. The acreage which could provide an adequate standard of living for a farmer and his family only a generation ago is now too small to do so, and the minimal size of a farm is constantly increasing. The farmer who finds himself with an undersized farm has two basic alternatives. One is to supplement his farm income by taking a job off the farm. In this case he may continue to farm the land himself, on a casual part-time basis, or he may lease his fields to a neighboring farmer. The other alternative is to "put together" a farm of adequate size by leasing land from neighbors who are no longer farming it.

The man employed in a factory usually works there no more than eight hours a day, and he may choose to use the hours before he leaves for work in the morning, or after he returns home in the evening, to farm his land. He may hire a neighboring farmer to perform certain necessary farm operations for him under contract, and he can arrange to have his annual vacation fall at the busiest season of the farm year, whether it be planting, harvest, or some other time.

Eventually, however, this becomes onerous, and the man who owns the land may lease it to one of his neighbors. The farmer who owns only part of the land he farms, and leases the remainder from his neighbors, is known as a "part-owner" farmer. Two factors seem to explain the rapid increase in the number of part-owner farmers in recent years. One is the reluctance of many rural landowners to sell land which has been in their families for several generations. The other is the steady increase in the cost of farm land. Taking the United States as a whole, the average per acre value of farm land has been rising about 5 per cent a year since World War II. Many farmers cannot afford to buy the additional land they need for an efficient farm operation; leasing it is the only practical method by which they can expand.

The farmer who buys or leases additional farm land always hopes that the new land will be close to that which he already farms, but in many instances this is not the case. In some areas quite a high proportion of farm operations—in contrast to farm ownership units—consist of two or more pieces of land which are not contiguous, and the farmer must move his machinery, equipment, and sometimes even his livestock from one piece of land to another which is some little distance away. A farm which consists of two or more scattered plots of land has no optimal location for the farm residence. It is remarkable that more American farmers have not moved their homes to urban areas, whence they could easily commute to the land they farm.

The only part of the nation where this appears to have occurred on any large scale is the wheat districts of the Great Plains, which reach from Texas northward to the Canadian border. Perhaps two thirds of all the work which needs to be done on a wheat farm is compressed into little more than six weeks. For the remainder of the year the farmer may live where he chooses. Some live in nearby small towns and are called "sidewalk farmers." Others take advantage of latitudinal variations in the seasons of planting and harvesting, and follow the crop northward twice a year. These are the "suitcase farmers" who do not even live in the area in which their lands are located. High-speed automobile highways and light private airplanes have contributed to the development of these farming systems.

The declining acreage of farm land, the increasing size of farms, and the declining farm population have worked serious hardships on the economy of small rural market centers, the hamlets and villages which have grown up to serve the local rural economy. In the Middle West, at least, it would appear that the spacing of such market centers is related to the density of the farm population, which in turn is a function of the size of farm units. Market centers are thickest on the ground, for example, in the eastern Middle Western United States, where most farms run about 80 to 120 acres. In Iowa, where farms run 160 to 200 acres, they are somewhat more sparse; and they are sparsest of all in central Illinois, where the farms are largest.

A declining farm population means that there are fewer people in the surrounding countryside to be served. The automobile has given them greater mobility so they can now bypass the small market center and seek the wider range of goods and services which are available in the larger towns and cities. The traveler who passes through one of the smaller market centers and sees ancient store fronts, boarded up and broken windows, and grass growing in the cracks in the sidewalk, concludes that these small market centers are dying.

This is only partially correct, at least in the Middle West, because the population of most of these small market places has continued to grow, despite their stagnating and dying economies.

This is partly due to long-distance commuting. The young family with many children can find cheaper housing here than in the city where the father works. The widow who is living on a tiny pension, or the divorcee who is raising a family on scanty alimony, also find that living is cheaper here. Perhaps this is only a temporary situation, but thus far these places have continued to grow in population despite their economic decline.

In recent years, two factors have had especially profound effects on the American countryside. One is the role of the government. The research and educational activities of governmental and private agencies have contributed greatly to increases in agricultural production by developing and disseminating information about better machinery, better agricultural chemicals, better biological strains of plants and animals, and better systems of farm management. On the other hand, governmental programs designed to reduce production by restricting crop acreages have tended to fossilize agricultural production in the geographical patterns of three decades ago.

For example, take the extreme case of cotton. The government guaranteed the cotton farmer a set price for his crop but restricted the acreage he was permitted to plant. In theory, this restriction of acreage should have reduced cotton production, but each farmer planted his allotted acreage (known as his "allotment") on his very best land, crammed the plants closer together in the rows, and poured on the fertilizer. The result has been a steady rise in cotton yields per acre and a steady increase in cotton production, despite almost continuous reduction of the acreage planted to cotton.

Furthermore, farmers have been reluctant to give up their acreage allotments even when they have been able to grow the crop at only a slim profit. The guaranteed price has enabled many farmers in the old Cotton Belt of the Southeast to continue growing cotton despite the high cost of producing it there, whereas acreage restrictions have prevented a greater increase in cotton production in the irrigated areas of the Southwest, where the crop can be grown much more cheaply. In this way, the government has fossilized agricultural production in some areas and prevented expansion and new developments in others.

The second factor which has profoundly modified the country-side is the impact of an opulent urban society. Rare indeed is the rural area in the United States which has not been changed in one way or another by urban influence, but some rural areas have been profoundly modified by wealthy urbanites. Because these people like to see well-kept fields and pastures, and can afford to pay for them, they have created some of the most beautiful rural landscapes in the United States. Showplace gentleman farms can be found near most of our major cities, but perhaps their most remarkable development is associated with the belt of cities which stretches along the east coast from Washington to Boston. Another area famous for its rural beauty is the Bluegrass country of Kentucky, whose horse farms are renowned for their stately mansions and lush green pastures dotted with shade trees and enclosed by white board fences.

But the gentleman farm is not the only rural manifestation of our opulent urban society, for today many farmers cultivate rec-reationists almost as assiduously as they cultivate crops. Dude ranches are springing up all over the nation, and many farmers so manage their land that it can be rented as a shooting preserve. In certain areas, in fact, wealthy men have acquired large acreages which are managed primarily as shooting preserves.

This is but another indication that the American countryside has become, to an even larger degree, an extension of the city. Agricultural production has been increasing steadily, but it has become more and more concentrated on the better lands. The remaining farms are growing larger, and more efficient, while vast acreages of marginal agricultural land, which once were pro-ductive, have gone out of farming in recent years.

Meantime, our growing, opulent, urban population is making

ever greater demands for more land, land for residence and land for recreation. The onetime farmer now commutes to a city job, while the countryside is filling up with former city people, and the old distinction between country bumpkin and city slicker has almost completely disappeared. And so it is that many parts of the nation are witnessing the paradoxical spectacle of agricultural abandonment and urban reoccupance of the land, which are occurring simultaneously.

SUGGESTED READINGS

Higbee, E. C., *The American Oasis: The Land and Its Uses.* New York: Alfred A. Knopf, 1957.

Marschner, F. M., *Land Use and Its Patterns in the United States.* Washington, D.C.: U.S. Government Printing Office, 1959.

Taylor, C. C., Ensminger, D., Longmore, T. W., Ducoff, L. J., Raper, A. F., Hagood, Margaret Jarman, McKain, W. C., Jr., and Schuler, E. A., *Rural Life in the United States.* New York: Alfred A. Knopf, 1949.

7 FARMS AND FARMING IN THE AMERICAN MIDWEST

Walter M. Kollmorgen

The image of abundance in the United States finds its main focus in the Midwest. Here is an extraordinarily large tract of good agricultural land which has responded with high and increasing crop yields to all manner of technological innovations. The agricultural productivity of this area has been enhanced by industry, which is based largely on local and bordering resources, prominent among which are coal, iron ore, and petroleum. River, lake —Great Lakes—and railroad transportation plus trucks and highways have joined the area effectively, internally and externally, so that the Midwest has truly become the vast hub of America's plenty.

Agriculture usually suggests food and fiber, but for the Midwest it is food and feeds. Most of the products harvested from the fields of the Midwest are feeds for animals. Next comes food for man, for whom a generous diet is produced, including such rich protein foods as pork, beef, poultry, eggs, milk, cheese, and butter. By world standards, this is a rich and perhaps wasteful diet in that about 80 per cent of the nutritive value of feeds is lost in animal growth and production. However, animal products as food represent a higher value category than feeds, and by American standards are basic and essential.

The area of the agricultural Midwest encompasses western Ohio, most of Indiana and Illinois, the southern parts of Michigan, Wisconsin, and Minnesota, all of Iowa, northern Missouri, northeast Kansas, and portions of eastern Nebraska, South Dakota, and perhaps North Dakota (Figure 7–1). The heart of the agricultural Midwest is certainly that part of the United States south and west of the Great Lakes which was glacially flattened, filled in, and enriched by the ice ages. To the north lie extensive areas of glacially impoverished land—northern Minnesota, Wisconsin, and Michigan—and to the south lie dissected areas with old, leached, and poorer soils. The western border reaches the Sandhills of Nebraska and the unglaciated, dissected lands west of the Missouri River in South Dakota. In general, the western border lies along a zone where crops and land use need to be geared to declining and more variable precipitation. Dependable moisture, particularly in summer, is essential for corn production, which plays a prominent role in the Corn Belt, the heart of the Midwest.

Although the well-endowed land of the Midwest is noted for good, sustained, and ever increasing yields per acre, of equal and perhaps greater importance is the high output per farmer and per worker. The fact that every agricultural worker in the United States feeds at least thirty-four other consumers suggests high efficiency. High output per worker calls for farms of ample size, and large farms call for mechanization. In the Midwest, farms are large by world standards, and they are getting larger under a relatively free and competitive system. How has this growth in size been possible in the face of rapid growth of local as well as national and world population?

About a century ago the farmers of the Midwest as well as the political and economic leaders of the country seemed to have made an important discovery in the 160-acre farm. Such a tract could be tilled reasonably well with family labor, using the power of horse shanks and the relatively simple tools of the day. And so the 160-acre farm, ample for its purpose in its day, was enshrined in the Homestead Act of 1862. Much of the land in the

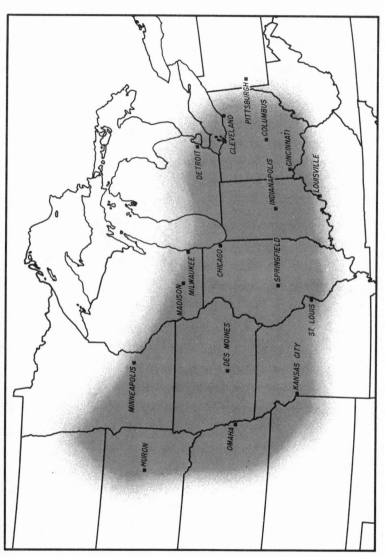

Figure 7-1. The agricultural Midwest. Agriculturally the American Midwest approximates the Corn Belt, or the Corn-Hog Belt; both these terms are somewhat loosely associated with the glacially enriched and partly loess-covered area south and west of the Great Lakes. The southern and eastern border shown on the map extends somewhat beyond the glacially enriched and better agricultural lands.

Midwest, particularly in the western and northern parts, was transferred to private ownership under this act, the pioneer settlers thus beginning with what seemed ample holdings. From then on, large families, rapid population growth, and, for a time, somewhat limited industrial growth, could have served to fragment farm sizes, and, indirectly, to reduce the output per worker. Fortunately, the larger geographical setting of the occupied Midwest prevented the development of this threat to farm size. Until the late nineteenth century, new settlements could be pushed westward and northward, reaching as far as the Pacific Ocean. In fact, most of the Plains wheat belts, the irrigated oases of the dry West, and the richly variegated farming patterns of the Pacific Coast did not develop fully until after 1900. Young would-be farmers therefore did not have to remain within the Midwest, settling down on small, fragmented farms, but found opportunities in the emerging farming areas on the Plains, in the Mountain West, or on the Pacific Coast. This leap-frog method of advance stopped only on the shores of the Pacific.

Rapid industrialization and urbanization in the Midwest and along its borders after the Civil War also drained off excess workers from rural areas, and so prevented the fragmentation of farm holdings. In a few short decades the Midwest became the foundry of the nation. In short order it gave us the railroad age, the farm machinery age, the tractor age, the automobile age, and, in general, provided most of the iron and steel that harnessed and applied inanimate power. Processing of farm products grew apace, and so did the trek to the city. Farms in the Midwest were not reduced in size with expanding population but actually increased in size.

While new lands and new off-farm jobs kept Midwest farms from splintering into smaller units providing mostly subsistence —as was and is true of so much of early Europe and Asia—new, bigger, and more expensive farm implements constantly prodded for bigger operating units, particularly outside certain specialized areas, such as the dairy and fruit belts. For a while, many farmers resisted this prodding by expanding livestock enterprises, such as feeding cattle, producing pork, milking cows for milk, cream, and butter production, or increasing flocks of poultry. While some of these arrangements still help to increase income on small acreages, they serve less and less to preserve the smaller farmer. Automation and specialization have entered the picture. Livestock feeding has become automated; the pressure is to replace workers with equipment and to have fewer workers serve more acres and animals. The extreme example of relocation and specialization is the poultry industry, which has moved out of the Midwest to the South, East, and Far West. Under specialization, it is not uncommon to find operations which handle several tens of thousands, even several hundred thousand, birds. Most of the grains fed to the birds, however, come from the Midwest. Formerly, nearly every farmer in the Midwest kept a flock of chickens which provided grocery money for the family or spending money for the wife, who frequently tended the flock. Now most farmers purchase eggs, milk, and butter or margarine.

In the heart of the Midwest lies the so-called Corn Belt or Corn-Hog Belt, and in the heart of this we now have a much smaller Soybean Belt in central Illinois. These terms do not mean that corn or soybeans prevail on the majority of agricultural acres in their respective belts, but rather that corn or soybeans exceed the respective acreages of other crops. In many counties, corn occupies about 40 to 50 per cent of the cropland.

This heavy dependence on corn rests largely on its high productivity per acre, in the form of either grain or silage. This high productivity is suggested by what are considered good average yields on a Corn Belt farm, namely: corn, 100 to 120 bushels per acre; oats, 50 to 60 bushels; wheat, 30 bushels; barley, 50 bushels; and soybeans, about 35 bushels. While wheat or soybeans has a higher value per pound or per bushel, the much higher yielding corn promises greater returns. The relative advantages of corn are stretched even further when the large five- to eight-foot plant plus ear is converted into silage and fed as roughage for cattle. A field that will yield 100 bushels of corn per acre could well yield 20 tons of silage per acre, which is the cheapest form of roughage a dairy farmer and cattle feeder can use.

The strong position corn occupies in diversified farming programs of the Midwest has been strengthened since World War II by the breakthrough in per-acre yields. Up to about two decades ago, 75 bushel yields were considered good, and 100 bushel yields outstanding. Now, good to outstanding yields range from 100 to 150 bushels per acre, and many farmers set themselves even higher goals. How has this breakthrough been achieved?

The peculiar nature of the plant has made it relatively simple to hybridize corn and to develop all manner of special qualities in root, stalk, and ear. So convincing have been the results in yields that practically all seed corn is now produced by plant breeders. The improved seed is planted by the farmer in much thicker stands than formerly. Where about 10,000 plants per acre were considered normal several decades ago, many fields now carry nearly 20,000 plants per acre, and efforts are being made to achieve 30,000 plants per acre. Needless to say, more plants per acre require more soil nutrients, and these are supplied by enlarged amounts of commercial fertilizer in several applications. The first, applied before plowing, is called "plow-down fertilizer." The next, usually accompanying planting, is termed "starter fertilizer." After some growth of the young plants comes a third, called "side dressing." Thus it is estimated that in Iowa the application of nitrogen to corn fields alone increased from less than 4 million tons in 1947 to 122 million tons in 1962.[1] Chemical warfare on weeds and pests has been joined to commercial fertilizer to enhance corn yields. Pesticides and herbicides are ap-

[1] L. H. Shaw and D. D. Durost, *The Effect of Weather and Technology on Corn Yields in the Corn Belt, 1929–62* (Washington, D.C.: U.S. Department of Agriculture, Economic Report No. 80, July 1965), p. 39.

plied to kill or inhibit insects and weeds. If these practices are accompanied by favorable weather, in terms of rainfall, temperature, and absence of hail, a bonanza crop is expected.

The breakthrough in corn yields also rests in part in other practices. Under acreage control programs, the best paying crops are usually planted on the best yielding fields in a farm complex. American farmers generally plant their allotted acres of corn, wheat, potatoes, cotton, and tobacco on the best available land. This choice of site in combination with other practices has, in large measure, cancelled out acreage limitations.

Political efforts to match American agricultural production to market demands at reasonable prices have had only limited success, largely because programs have been based on acreage allotment rather than on product control. Although numerous examples could be cited, such as wheat, cotton, potatoes, and tobacco, consider briefly the trends in acreage, yield, and production of feed grains. If 1954 is selected as the base year representing 100, acreage of feed grain harvested has been reduced 25 per cent; production, however, has increased by 40 per cent and yield per acre by 80 per cent. Although corn played a major role in this explosion of yields, crop yields of other feeds have also edged upward. Soybeans, only partly a feed grain crop, showed the most modest increase, only 18 per cent. The above figures, however, also cover grain sorghums, which are only now edging into the Corn Belt from the Southwest. These have shown an increase in yields of 119 per cent during this same decade. This spectacular increase reflects use of improved and adapted varieties, increased irrigation in the Southwest, several years of favorable growth conditions in the Wheat-Sorghum Belt, and movement of this crop into the higher rainfall areas of the Midwest.

Until recently, the farmer of the Midwest was dedicated to both corn production and crop rotations. Rotation usually meant that a crop of small grain, such as oats, barley, or wheat, followed corn; a hay crop, preferably alfalfa or red clover, followed a small grain. A legume, such as alfalfa, not only provided a good yield of nutritious hay, but also added nitrogen to the soil, an important consideration before the use of commercial nitrogen. Small grains also played their role as feed crops, cash crops, and nurse crops for legumes; they provided straw for bedding animals, served to diversify climatic and price risks, and offered the farmer a sustained, even work load in field operations. In addition, diversification offered some advantages from the standpoint of weed and pest control.

Changing technology has made crop diversification and rotation less necessary, and so a tendency to grow fewer crops is discernible in parts of the Midwest. Legume crops are no longer necessary to achieve nitrogen in the soil. Failure to plant a legume crop renders a nurse crop of small grains less attractive. Soybeans are not in surplus, command a relatively good price, and have expanded rapidly in acreage. Hence some of the better sections of the Midwest—central Illinois, much of northern Iowa, and southern Minnesota—are concentrating more and more on corn and soybeans at the expense of hay crops and small grains. Consequently we hear more and more about sustained periods of corn production, periods lasting from five to ten years, and even longer. Trends therefore indicate a tendency to specialize more and diversify less in crop and livestock production.

The animal population on Midwest farms has decreased in variety and types, but in many instances the fewer remaining types have increased in numbers. Horses declined rapidly after World War I and chickens disappeared from farmyards after World War II. The production of fryers and eggs has either been concentrated in large mass production units locally or has shifted to other sections of the country. Actually, much poultry meat now consumed in the Midwest is imported from Arkansas or Georgia and adjacent states. Milk production has become specialized in concentrated areas near urban centers and in the Dairy Belt on the northern border of the Corn Belt.

The remarkable shift of the fryer industry, during recent decades, to the Southern, Eastern, and Far Western states is closely related to the high conversion of specially prepared feeds to meat by improved breeds of chickens. This ratio is now approaching two to one, and the young birds reach processing age—about three pounds—in ten to twelve weeks. Hence it appears economical to ship Midwest feeds to the new poultry centers where some advantages accrue because of labor costs, markets, and, in part, climatic considerations.

The hog ranks next to the chicken as an efficient converter of prepared feeds into meat. Good farm operators convert four to five pounds of feed to one pound of live pork, and marketable animals—200 to 240 pounds—are produced in five to six months. Large doses of forage are not essential in an accelerated program of pork production. Hence there is more and more confinement of hogs in small open yards or in buildings, with or without slatted floors. Hogs used for breeding stock, of course, still profit from exercise, sunlight, and fresh air, best found in a good pasture, preferably a good alfalfa field.

The above observations give some clues as to why the hog is popular in the Midwest and why some writers use the term Corn-Hog Belt. Feed is produced in abundance but, in most instances, only limited acreages are set aside for pasture. Hogs do not require as much space as cattle, only breeding stock is turned out to forage. Also, hog breeding can be cycled faster than cattle breeding, with two pig litters a year; this yields financial benefits in more frequent sales and less long-time financing. For these reasons, the generally smaller farms in the eastern part of the Corn Belt and certain parts of the Dairy Belt give more emphasis to pork production than to beef production.

A discernible tendency in the hog industry is the separation of breeding and feeding. The hog breeder produces feeder pigs which after weaning are sold to hog feeders. The latter may have highly concentrated improvements, providing for close hog con-

83

finement, and all manner of equipment for feed preparation and automatic feeding. Here is another example of how technology and big capital requirements are squeezing the small diversified farmer.

The Midwest, and more particularly the Corn Belt, cannot be disassociated from corn-fed beef, one of the most highly prized foods on the American table. In the American setting, good beef production requires both forage and fattening grain. Both are found in the Midwest, although pastures used for the production of forage decline in size and importance in the better grain-producing areas. Conversely, areas in the Midwest with land that is rough, poorly drained, or otherwise marginal maintain significant acreages in pasture. Most of these pastures, outside the Dairy Belt, are grazed by beef cattle, and many of the beef cattle are foundation herds used to raise calves. In about a year, these calves become feeder cattle and then are placed in feed lots for fattening. However, the grain-growing Midwest does not produce enough feeder cattle to fill all its feed lots, and so additional feeders are shipped in, mainly from the grasslands of the West, but considerable numbers also come from the Gulf Coastal states and the South Atlantic states.

The conversion ratio of feed to animal weight is lower and more variable for cattle than for poultry and hogs because of the greater use of roughage for cattle. A feed combination including one or two pounds of hay may well yield one pound of animal weight for eight pounds of feed. Corn silage—including the chopped ears—may be substituted for part of the dry grain, but the conversion ratio will be lower because of increased moisture and fiber content of the feed.

Only a few decades ago, feed lots used for fattening cattle were largely limited to the Midwest Corn Belt, where they were and still are largely unspecialized operations in diversified farming programs. On most of these operations less than 100 cattle are fattened per year, although all sorts of labor-saving devices may be used in preparing and serving the feeds. In sharp contrast stand the large, specialized feed lots which have recently developed in the southern Great Plains, in New Mexico and Arizona, and particularly in California. The contrast in sizes of operations is striking. For example, Iowa, the leading cattle-feeding state, reported that 54,651 farms marketed grain-fed cattle in 1961. In this same year, about 600 large feed lots in California fattened enough cattle to make that state rank second in the United States in this enterprise. At least a score of these operations turned out between 25,000 to 50,000 fattened cattle per year. In the Corn Belt, cattle-feeding operations handling 10,000 cattle per year are still unusual and still play a minor role in total beef output. To what extent the large operations will expand in the Midwest is still a moot question. Every grain farm in the Midwest produces roughages of various kinds which can sustain beef cattle at certain stages of development, and failure to use them may bring diseconomies.

The rather phenomenal increase in milo production during the last two decades, as a complementary crop to wheat in the Winter Wheat Belt, has served to attract more and more cattle-feeding operations to the southern Great Plains. Milo is considered 90 per cent as good as corn for feeding and fattening, and its volume production has already served to dot the area with many feeding operations, many of the large, specialized types. In total, the feed lot belt is expanding from the Midwest Corn Belt through the Wheat-Milo Belt of the Southwest and terminating in the huge lots in California. This means, of course, that feeder cattle produced in the Southwest, and even the South, may move in several directions to feeders, processors, and consumers.

The geographic spread of feed lots to the Southwest and California, in combination with population growth, particularly in California, has resulted in increased competition for feeders produced in that part of the country and has in part reduced the movement of these animals to the Corn Belt. This development, in turn, has encouraged the expansion of breeding herds in the Midwest. For example, cow herds in Illinois nearly doubled from 1951 to 1963, and the number of cows increased from 404,000 to 730,000 during this same period. This change in cow population enables the state to produce about 40 per cent of its feeders.

Expansion of cow herds also means expansion and improvements of pasture. Although the best cropland sites are rarely converted to pasture, enough slope lands and somewhat marginal sites along streams and valleys allow for this conversion. In large measure, however, the increase in number of cows is supported by improved pastures with substantially increased forage yields. Up to a decade or two ago, most pastures in the Midwest were essentially exercise lots which contained poor, weedy stands of bluegrass. These pastures were rarely limed or fertilized. The result was that it required several acres to sustain a cow with even a moderate feed supply. Then came brome grass and familiarity with commercial fertilizers and lime. A good brome pasture properly fertilized can carry a cow and calf, on an acre or two, for six months and produce from 300 to 400 pounds of beef per acre. Forage yields on these improved pastures may well be from four to six times as high as on the former weedy pastures. It follows that land conversion from grain crops to grass crops need not be in the same proportion as the increase in cow population.

On the northern margin of the Midwest, and extending eastward, lies the Dairy Belt, where beef cattle yield to dairy cattle in numbers and attention. This belt begins in southeastern Minnesota, extends across southern Wisconsin, accompanies the industrial belt south of the Great Lakes, and extends eastward to the Megalopolis along the Mid and North Atlantic coast. However, for quantity and variety of production—milk, milk powder, condensed and evaporated milk, butter, and cheese—Wisconsin, Minnesota, and Michigan hold leading positions. Thus a major portion of the Dairy Belt lies in the Midwest.

Dairy farms are generally smaller than diversified farms, usually have better improvements for sheltering cattle and feeds, and frequently encompass marginal land which is unsuited for crop farming but which may serve well for pasture. Marginality is often the product of glaciation which has left marshy and wet tracts, boulder-strewn fields, or sandy and gravelly soil patches of limited productivity. The proximity of the dairy area to the urban and industrial belt should also be noted in that concentrations of population provide a ready market for much of the milk produced.

The milk cow, as against the beef cow, is a demanding guest in terms of time and attention. Not only should a dairy cow be milked twice a day, but this chore should also come very nearly at the same hours every day. On a dairy farm, therefore, the dairy herd is usually central, not only in the work program but also in the production of feed and fodder on available land. Farm income is limited largely to the sale of milk or milk products, and also dairy animals. Although dairy farmers in good marketing areas have a reasonably good income, and one well distributed throughout the year, dairy farms usually do not attract speculative investments, particularly from nonfarm sources. A good tenant for a dairy farm of small to average size is very difficult to find. The result is that a higher percentage of dairy farms in the Dairy Belt are owner operated than is true of farms in high-yielding cash-grain farming areas of the Midwest.

Dairy farms have always been the main source of young animals—mostly male—converted to veal. Veal production, however, has declined sharply in this country during recent years, largely because young dairy stock is grown to maturity and sold as beef. Although this beef may lack some of the quality of meat coming from fattened beef types (which is reflected in market prices) young animals with Holstein blood make rapid gains and yield much good meat, including large quantities of good hamburger, so popular with American youngsters. Numerous dairy farmers now engage in the secondary activity of raising and fattening a herd of dairy animals. This practice has to some extent served to replace hog production, which has frequently been a secondary activity on those dairy farms with enough land to produce necessary feeds.

Technological changes have by no means bypassed the American dairy farmer. Mechanical milking equipment is taken for granted, and so are all manner of arrangments for sanitation and rapid cooling of milk. Selective breeding and culling are almost mandatory to assure high milk yields. The use of balanced feeds, also referred to as hot feeds, is almost universal, with the result that milk and butterfat yields per cow have reached high levels. Herds with average yields of milk approaching 15,000 pounds per animal are becoming commonplace. The result is that the dairy products of this country are being supplied by a declining number of dairy animals, although the total cattle population has reached new highs of over 100 million—about 106 million.

While the American Midwest farming area stands alone in the world in terms of areal extent and output of feeds and foods, it would be misleading not to mention certain trends which bespeak problems. Space considerations require that these observations be brief and selective.

Part of the problem faced by the American food producer is that the prices of the products he markets are declining while the retail prices of processed foods to the consumer are increasing. This point is well illustrated in a recently released publication of the United States Department of Agriculture which states in part:

> Retail prices of food products originating on American farms have been climbing slowly much of the time since World War II. But prices farmers received for these products have declined. Rising marketing charges have prevented retail food prices from declining with farm prices. In 1964, retail prices of farm-originated foods averaged 14 per cent higher than in 1947–49. Their farm value, however, was 15 per cent lower than in the early post-war period. Marketing charges were up 43 per cent.[2]

[2] United States Department of Agriculture, *Food Costs*, Miscellaneous Publication No. 856, revised August 1965 (Washington, D.C.: Economics Research Service).

Paradoxically, the decline in prices received by farmers was accompanied by an increase in the value of farm land. Such increases have ranged from 3 to 6 per cent per year since World War II, and the end is not in sight. Marked increases have also occurred in labor costs, machinery, and other input items, so that profitable farming is more of a hope than fact. In reality, many farmers realize no profit at all in a good bookkeeping sense, and must count as a modest wage the minuscule cash balance—if any —achieved at the end of the year. The most dependable reward awaiting the American farmer is the increased value of the land he farms. Why then the increased land values?

Declining farm prices serve almost universally as a lash to increase output. More output can be achieved by operating more acres, and hence the tendency to pay extra for additional farm land. Add to this the purchase of land by urban investors who try to hedge against inflation or to gain certain income tax advantages or who look with loving sentiment on a bit of rural America, and the rationale begins to take form. After all, population is exploding in numbers, food is already short in most parts of the world, and the Good Lord is not making any more good acres that promise food for the hungry.

Those inclined to question some of these observations need only be reminded of several striking developments in American agriculture. Only several decades ago there were over 6 million farmers in this country; now there are about 3 million. It is expected that this number will again be cut in half, probably within less than a decade. This is a remarkable prospect because the average farm worker already feeds thirty-four mouths, and within less than a decade he may well feed over fifty mouths. Extinction is therefore the reward for efficient food production— at least to a degree. Machinery and technology are replacing manpower. The fact that disproportionate numbers of farmers are aged and even over-aged in terms of a dynamic working force tempers to a degree the decimation of their ranks.

Averages, however, mean little in the dynamic, competitive, and hazardous game of farming. We should therefore also note that only about 25 per cent of American farmers produce about 75 per cent of the products marketed. Obviously, the "average farmer" does not command the land, the capital, and perhaps the know-how to survive as an entrepreneur in rural America.

Farming in the Midwest, and elsewhere in the United States, is heading in the direction of corporate enterprises, particularly within family units. A few sample cost figures suggest the need for this direction. Good cropland in the Midwest already ranges from $300 to $1,000 per acre. With good but expensive machinery a farmer can operate from 320 to 640 acres. As an example, 400 acres of $500 land would call for an investment of $200,000. An additional investment of $50,000 in machinery and livestock means an enterprise costing a quarter of a million dollars. This is a far cry from the nearly free land provided by the Homestead Act a century ago. Obviously, few young men can still aspire to farm ownership unless this is made possible by an inheritance. Nor can a farm of high value be handed down readily in an inheritance program where there are multiple children, without laying a heavy burden of debt on the new operator. Family and nonfamily corporate holdings therefore appear more and more conspicuously on the horizon.

Americans should forever be grateful for the endowment of the Midwest in terms of both agriculture and industry. The harvest in foods and industrial products has been enormous. The harvest in guide lines, particularly in the field of institutional arrangments, has been meager. Even if some of the physical endowments of the Midwest can be matched elsewhere, times and circumstances have changed, and so its development or present patterns cannot be duplicated or re-created. Here as elsewhere the search will go on to find the men and the institutional arrangements needed to provide the elemental needs of food, clothing, and shelter.

SUGGESTED READINGS

Garland, J. H., "The Heart of a Continent," Chapter 1 in J. H. Garland (ed.), *The North American Midwest, A Regional Geography.* New York: John Wiley & Sons, 1955.

Higbee, E., *American Agriculture: Geography, Resources, Conservation.* New York: John Wiley & Sons, 1958.

Hutton, G., *Midwest at Noon.* Chicago: University of Chicago Press, 1946.

Kollmorgen, W. M., "Significance of Agriculture," Chapter 4 in J. H. Garland (ed.), *The North American Midwest, A Regional Geography.* New York: John Wiley & Sons, 1955.

Weaver, J. C., "Changing Patterns of Cropland Use in the Middle West." *Economic Geography,* XXX (January 1954), 1–47.

Weaver, J. C., "Crop-Combination Regions in the Middle West." *The Geographical Review,* XLIV, No. 2 (1954), 175–200.

8 THE GEOGRAPHY OF POVERTY IN THE UNITED STATES

Gordon E. Reckord

INTRODUCTION

America is only now beginning to understand the geographical characteristics and consequences of the phenomenon of poverty. Poverty is a complex idea made up of relative associations of other ideas. Only recently, beginning with the great depression of the 1930's, has it been considered a worthwhile subject for serious nationwide research. A rising interest in the incidence of poverty, generated in part by a high national prosperity and a great wave of social legislation, has demanded the collection and notation of better and more precise statistical descriptions of poverty for smaller local areas.

More precise definitions of local distress and the illumination given by these facts have prompted the inauguration of new programs for the relief of poverty. Differences in income levels and unemployment between urban and non-urban areas and between parts of the city have highlighted the need for the attack upon poverty and have brought about a public appreciation that poverty occurs in locational patterns. The serious problems of poverty in the great city where the burden is unevenly distributed within particular groups has been brought into sharp focus. The adjustment costs which are a concomitant of the powerful forces that have given rise to the great city have alerted the general public which has in turn, in a period of general prosperity, given authority to the federal government to give increasing attention to the poor.

The purpose of this brief exploration of the geography of poverty in America is to highlight the nature of its distribution, or maldistribution, to explore the causes of that distribution in interrelationship with other phenomena, and to indicate what steps are being taken to eliminate poverty where it exists.

WHO IS POOR?

Measurements of poverty, and especially the comparative study of poverty by kind and place, are neither simple nor easy. Poverty is always relative—what is poor to one is not to another. Needs vary from place to place. Individual desires are conditional.

Poverty is seldom absolute. There is no way to measure accurately the extent of unfulfilled needs that are characteristic of a given group. Need is a reflection of the goals that are established by the individual and his culture group. A family's needs will depend on the size of the family, the general state of the health of its members, the number and conditions of their material possessions or assets, their ability and willingness to save and to plan for the future, and the level of spending they encounter among friends and neighbors.

If the minimum standard of American living is taken as the norm, then most of the world's inhabitants are poor by comparison. The African tribal leader is poor when measured against the wealth of an American steelworker; and the poverty of his subjects is almost immeasurably greater. A comfortable American frontiersman of a hundred years ago would be in abject poverty if measured by today's standards.

Victor R. Fuchs of the National Bureau of Economic Research sums up the problem of the relativity of poverty:

by the absolute standards that have prevailed over most of the world's history, and still prevail over large areas of the world, there are very few poor in the United States today. Nevertheless, there are millions of American families who, both in their own eyes and those of others, are poor. As our nation prospers, our judgment as to what constitutes an "insufficiency" of goods and services will inevitably change. Today's comfort or convenience is yesterday's luxury and tomorrow's necessity. In a dynamic democratic society, how could it be otherwise? [1]

There is consensus that the level of poverty in the United States starts at the family income level of about $3,000 per family. Any amount less than that level indicates in some degree a standard intolerable to the rest of the population. Such a definition is arbitrary because it will include some families which for one reason or another are not impoverished—living in a particularly favorable place, with small family needs or having particularly apt household management. That family's condition is not intolerable to the rest of society. At the same time, the definition does not include other families which even with a higher income may in fact be poor and may in fact impose a burden on others. With few exceptions, a family earning $3,000 or less lives without surety of the future; this level of income means that the cost of advanced education for the sons and daughters of the family will need to come from outside the family; there will be few if any purchases of new goods or outside services including health; almost certainly it means the minimum expenditure for clothing, food, and shelter and that cultural pursuits will be those engendered only within the family. It sometimes means geographic and cultural isolation from other families even at the same income.

In 1962, there were 47 million families in the United States. About 9.3 million, or one fifth of these, had total money incomes

[1] Victor R. Fuchs, "The Concept of Poverty," in *Toward a Theory of Power*, First Report of the Task Force on Economic Growth and Opportunity, Study Paper (Washington, D.C.: United States Chamber of Commerce, 1965), p. 71.

of less than $3,000. Nearly 11 million of the 30 million people in these families were children. More than half of these families had incomes of less than $2,000. There was serious poverty among those who lived alone or who lived in boarding houses outside of families: about 5 million of these individuals had incomes of less than $1,500. Thus some 33 to 35 million Americans, or nearly one fifth of the nation's population, in 1962 were living at or below the threshold of poverty. This at a time when the median family income for the United States was nearly $6,000.

The characteristics of the people who make up these families are significant, including their pattern of geographic distribution. For instance, 17 per cent of poor families were headed by white persons in 1962 and more than three times that number had non-white family heads. Forty-eight per cent had a female at the head of the family in a society where the male head is usual. Seventy-six per cent of these family groups had no regular wage earners, and part-time employment was a regular way of living. Farmers made up the greatest percentage of employed family heads with la-borers and people employed in service trades at 30 and 27 per cent respectively. Seventy-five per cent of these family heads had pro-gressed to the eighth year of school only, and only 5 per cent had graduated from college.

The reasons for family poverty are extremely difficult to isolate and describe. Usually there is more than one handicap that places the family at a disadvantage. And to place the family head in a single group may not disclose the reason for his membership in that group. Herman P. Miller, the noted American population statistician, believes that the perpetuation of low-income farms is the first cause of poverty. Advanced age is cited as the second most important disadvantage, followed in order by fatherless families or families without a male head, then families headed by non-white males under sixty-five years of age, and finally those fami-lies that are poor even though they do not have the other attri-butes of poor families. This latter group will include those who are technically white (Mexicans and Puerto Ricans) but who do not share the advantages that "whitehood" brings. Also in this group are young families which are just getting started, and those families headed by otherwise well-intentioned men who as our society describes them "simply do not have it." For reasons of intelligence, unwillingness, or lack of training, such family heads have low productivity. One American observer has expressed the belief that the number of members of this class will grow significantly, simply because the human race—at least that part of it living in North America—no longer fits the society in which it has to live. Our society just does not have jobs for certain kinds of people and "the number of such unemployables seems likely to grow rather rapidly."

In 1960, there were 1.5 million families which lived on farms and had yearly incomes of less than $3,000. Most of these families earned less than $2,000 each year, and even if one credits the family income with food produced on the farm they would still be poor. One out of every six of these farmers is nonwhite. Interestingly, the low-income farm population is no longer dominated by the Negro sharecropper as it was twenty years ago. Many of these families have left the land for the seemingly greater opportunities in urban places, only to be disappointed.

There were about 2.5 million advanced-age low-income families, predominantly white, headed by a person over sixty-five years of age. Most of the aged poor families were man and wife, many of them living on social security or other pensions or transfer payments. About 60 per cent of this group did no paid work. Of the fatherless family group, there were about 1.5 million families in 1960 without fathers in the home. About two in every three of these families were white.

Among the poor, there were in 1960 about 1 million families who were nonwhite and headed by a man under sixty-five years. One fourth of these family heads are employed as laborers, and an additional third are employed as domestics, or in the service trades. Thus about three out of every five of these low-paid family heads work in low paying occupations, and if low-paying factory workers are added, the percentage jumps to 85 per cent of all these poor nonwhite families.

As hinted before, the fifth group contains those whose poverty comes from some basic characteristics within themselves and for which there is no clearly observable explanation. To identify and offer solutions for this group is particularly difficult because so many different factors contribute to its being. Yet a collective decision must be made as to the identification of the group so as to provide the assistance necessary to reduce personal suffering and minimize the corrosive effect on society.

It is probable that the proportion of impoverished persons has declined in the United States. Sustained full employment and higher wages break down the barriers to mobility from class to class or from place to place. At such time, people leave the farm and nonwhite farmers leave more quickly than whites. Labor flows from low-income areas to high-income areas. People move because there is a better job to move to; social barriers fall in the scramble for workers. The difference between high and low income narrows. The reverse of all of these movements takes place with a decline of prosperity. The newest entrees to the labor force depart. Workers return to the farm from the city. Discrimination takes hold, and the disparity in income increases between groups.

The meanings of these movements to the members of the poverty group in the future are unclear. It does appear that the *relative* improvement in earnings is greater for low-income groups when industries transfer from high-wage areas to low-wage areas. Recent low-paid farm labor finds new higher-paying jobs in textile mills which have moved from New England to the South, as the New England textile workers remain behind to become skilled in electronics. However, as wage rates equalize, as transportation improves, as capital flows, the inequalities of income decline; and as general prosperity continues it may be that in the future the solution of the problems of the low-income groups will be more difficult.

THE ROVING POOR

The United States is fed by a factory of farms. The family farm, a basic concept in American agriculture, is giving way to the large commercial farm organization which complements the urban economy which in turn encourages such commercial organization. Modern technology permits a farm family, given sufficient capital, to manage even a large farm for most of the year. Efficiency in operation calls for the assembly of large parcels of land suited to efficient machine cultivation particularly in that part of the nation where soil, slope, and climatic conditions are favorable. The great Midwest, the low and high plains west of the Mississippi River, the riverine deltas in the South and West are suited to this kind of large-scale cash agriculture. Large parcels of land permit the introduction of specialized labor-saving machinery, with mechanical power increasing the efficiency of every man-hour used. Specialized farming requires application of artificial fertilizer, deep plowing, and special tillage methods including irrigation, and gives increasing yields per acre and permits nonrotation.

The need for extensive labor is limited to short periods of the year for planting, harvest, or processing. This, in turn, means that many of the laborers who at one time lived on the land where the crop was grown, subsisting partly on farm gardens, now can find a livelihood in agriculture only by working for cash wages when required.

The seasonality of farm production is the basic reason for the use of migrant labor in American agriculture. The crop year begins in the southern states where the harvest comes first with the new spring sun. Fresh vegetables and fruits are harvested and sped to the northern cities where winter is still at hand. Modern refrigeration and freight handling by specialized railroad cars and trucks make this possible. As the spring moves north, the migrant labor moves north, too, hiring out to large farm operators to harvest cash crops and to supplement locally available labor.

In 1962, there were about 380,000 migrant farmer workers in the United States. This means that one out of every ten of the people who were hired to work on farms had no permanent work place. Yet, for most of these workers, their meager earnings total more than could have been earned if they had stayed on their original homestead. The number of migrant workers has not declined as sharply as has the total farm labor force, mostly because these workers are concentrated in fruit and vegetable harvesting and cotton cultivation which have not been mechanized to the extent many other crops have.

About one fifth of the migrants who worked twenty-five days or more in 1962 were nonwhite, mostly Negroes. Four fifths of these workers were male. Over half of the migrants were young people, from fourteen to thirty-four years. Most of them had no work experience except hand or stoop labor. Schooling is difficult for youngsters as they move from place to place, and housing is oftentimes inadequate.

The distribution pattern of migrant workers varies by type and area. Negro migrant labor is mostly concentrated in the eastern seaboard migratory stream, from south to north. The Atlantic seaboard group begin their northward trip in Florida in citrus fruits and vegetables, moving north to the Carolinas, the Delaware Peninsula, and returning south in September when employment in tobacco, tomato, potato, and bean harvest slackens. Puerto Ricans swell this stream, with greater concentration in the northern portion of the seaboard, from spring to fall.

Another major pattern starts in California and Arizona in vegetables and citrus fruits, moving north along the Pacific Coast with sugar beets, fruits, berries, nuts, and vegetables. There is a mid-continent movement from the Rio Grande Valley in Texas, with sugar beets, bush berries, apples, fruits, and vegetables. California (January to December), Michigan (April to November), Texas, New York, Oregon, and Washington employed the largest number of migrant workers in 1963. Americans of Mexican origins predominate in the mid-continent and western migrant streams.

The changing geographic patterns of the nation's farm poor are obvious. National adjustment to changes in the efficient use of farm land has to be made by those who are victims of new efficiencies and at the same time less able to compete for the new jobs in the cities. Migrant farm laborers earn the least money per hour, suffer the disadvantage of an unstable home and associated social institution like schools, and by the very nature of their associations are less able to change their conditions either by transfer or by changes in their working conditions. It seems likely, however, that their conditions will change. New federal laws and regulations and productivity increases are narrowing the gap between wages paid for farm labor and wages of the rest of the worker force. Health, immunization practices, and living conditions are improving under the impact of social pressure and legislative action. Sooner or later the urban population will adjust to the added costs of this labor through its pricing system. The social program of the federal government will change the basic training and education of these people by special schools and courses so that the necessary labor will be performed only by those who are willing to do so for the rewards then available.

There are two distinguishing patterns of poverty in the United States. One is a dispersed pattern of families and individuals with absolute low income, not always associated with agriculture but living away from urban places. The other is a compact pattern of families and individuals living in cities. They are usually employed in the service or unskilled jobs that are typical of the complex industrial make-up of the cities in which they live.

THE URBAN POOR

More than half of all the families in the United States (54 per cent) who earn less than $3,000 live in urban places. These are the urban poor, constituting more than 5 million families that are consigned to the city by circumstances of origin, adjustment, fortune, and desire. The distribution of these urban poor is well recognized but not completely understood, and certainly at this time mapped only in general outline. By and large, the urban poor occupy the least desirable portions of our cities, and they include within their ranks the slum and the near-slum family.

Concentration of the poor in American cities is the expected outcome of an accelerating process of urban deterioration. Most American cities have been notorious and voracious consumers of land. Reflecting in part the relative cheapness of land not essential to the production of foodstuffs on which the city could expand, and the relative importance of transportation, there have been few if any appreciable barriers to expansion from the building of the first house, the paving of the first street network, or the construction of the first waterline. When these buildings, or these streets, or this sewer became outmoded, the easiest step was to rebuild on new land farther from the city center, leaving the vacated land or building to some other, usually more menial but sometimes more rewarding, task. The usual response of the city dweller, at least those who could afford to do so, was to move outward, too.

The next stage is familiar in the land use pattern of every American city. Most of the residential structures abandoned by one income group became the residences of another group several steps down the income ladder. The new tenants crowded in, and the living quarters were divided and subdivided. Maintenance and repair deteriorated, and the middle-class areas became slums.

The city slum is considered by many a mixture of the good and the bad. In simple romantic logic, it is a neighborhood of the minimum where the newcoming immigrant landed, braced his feet, and with little if any resources and with his old-country pride made a new start and took off for the American dream. Now the slum has become the locus of the stinging, grinding, lengthy, gradual adjustment that characterizes a white society's acceptance of different colored skin and custom. Michael Harrington, a champion of the dispossessed, observes that the "incredible American adventure of the ethnic slum is coming to an end," and the ethnic slum is being replaced by a new kind of slum. Its inhabitants include aged families from the old ethnic slum, and recent migrants from other cultures who, because of easily recognized physical attributes, find it more difficult than their predecessors to bridge the adjustment gap. For many the "this makes the ghetto walls are higher than they have ever been." No longer romantic, the slum is a problem which will not solve itself.

These slums have a solid base of poverty. Here gather the disabled, the untutored, the mentally ill, the aged, the sick, and their children. In the large cities, racial minorities form the important part of the slum population. The typical physical setting is depressing. Land use is mixed, and deterioration of buildings is routine. A description from a recent study is illuminating:

> Most of the . . . area may be characterized as an old one in which residential values have diminished or have been threatened by the encroachment of nonresidential land use, high population density, and physical deterioration. Many of the City's redevelopment and renewal programs, consequently, have been within the area, In fact, . . . the relatively small number of residential structures built after 1940 have been publically sponsored or financed.
>
> In addition to the extensive clearance projects, large segments of the study area have been designated as "conservation areas," and urban renewal and conservation programs have been initiated.

Despite redevelopment and rehabilitation, however, blighted conditions are still associated with much of the study area. Twenty-eight per cent of the housing units are either deteriorating or dilapidated in comparison with 10 per cent deteriorated or dilapidated units in the rest of the City. Although only 28 per cent of all the housing units in the City are in the study area, 50 per cent of all deteriorating units (77,743) and 56 per cent of all dilapidated units (17,428) are within these commuities.

Coupled with the high percentage of units in generally poor condition is a high percentage of units that are considered overcrowded. Twenty-two per cent of all housing units in the study area have more than 1.01 persons per room compared with 11.7 per cent for the City as a whole. Of the twenty community areas, only five have less than 11.7 per cent overcrowded housing units.

. . . one-third of the housing units in this subarea are either deteriorated or dilapidated, representing almost one-third of all the deteriorated and dilapidated units in the City. Within four of the ten communities of this subarea, the percentage of deteriorating and dilapidated units exceeds 40 per cent.

The study area has lost population during the last decade. Most of the decline resulted from an out-migration of the white population. An estimated 417,416 white persons moved out of the study area between 1950 and 1960, resulting in a net decrease of 356,924 white persons. This decrease has been offset in part by a net increase of 241,087 nonwhite persons.

In 1960, 60 per cent of the population in the study area was nonwhite. Perhaps more significantly, the 673,281 nonwhite persons in the study area represented 80 per cent of Chicago's nonwhite population. Further, it contained, in 1960, 82 per cent of the City's Negro population and 23 per cent of other nonwhite groups.[2]

The slum phenomenon in America has not yet been mapped. The large numbers of cities with slum areas, the precise location of the boundaries, the overwhelming problem of the statistical

[2] *Study of the Industrial Redevelopment Potential of a Core Section of Chicago*, Mayor's Committee for Economic and Cultural Development of Chicago (unpublished draft, Area Redevelopment Administration, U.S. Department of Commerce, Chicago, July 1965).

data baffle the American geographer who undertakes to study these areas. To solve the problem the electronic computer is a necessary working tool. It is apparent that it will be necessary to map the slum phenomenon, if for no other reason than that the allocation of available program resources under new public programs, including the poverty program and the Economic Development Act, requires identification of areas. Given the availability of a limited amount of investment dollars, it will be necessary to indicate precisely where the investment will take place. This will force the definition and mapping of specific areas and the appropriation of specific budget items to be applied to such areas.

There is a close correlation between the incidence of personal poverty and the features of the city landscape. Housing is the major location determinant of poverty: concentrations of city poverty will occur at those points in the city which offer shelter at minimal cost. The poorest occupant will select the absolute minimum rent that he can pay. This obviously will occur in buildings or dwellings that have no alternative use at that price or at a higher price. Since capital investment for alternate dwellings by the slum dweller is usually impossible, the price paid will be in rents. The price for rent will be higher if the renter, for reasons other than price, is unable to find alternate quarters.

There is a certain internal coalescence among these slum forces that gives rise to gradually enlarging areas of slum use, once the process is started. A group of residences, usually apartment buildings built during an earlier period at the outskirts of the city core, is no longer attractive to those who are able to pay higher rents in new apartments as well as the added costs of transportation to work from more detached locations. The owner of the apartment, who in time has fully amortized his investment, sells at an amortized cost to a new investor who is willing to speculate that the future need for land in this place near the city center will increase the worth of his holdings. He probably values the building at less than the value of his land. It is obvious that his lack of concern will take the form of further deterioration of the buildings, subsequent lower prices to renters, and the gradual concentration of these renters in districts where over a period of time the same forces on many properties accelerate and fortify the process. Additional research on the motives of investors in slum properties and incentives to changing slum land use seems likely to point to promising new directions for programs to relieve these conditions.

The trend is the same in every city slum. Higher and higher concentrations as families share the costs of living which are at best an overload on the poor family budget.

THE DISPERSED NON-URBAN PATTERN

There is a distinct two-part pattern to the incidence of non-urban poor in the United States. The first comprises several extensive regions of low income and heavy unemployment separated from each other and removed from the coastal lowlands. A list of major areas thus defined would include: Appalachia, Great Lakes Cut-over, Ozarka, Four Corners Indian Area, northern New England, and northern Rockies. The existence of these large areas reflects consistent and internally connected common problems most likely associated with regional physical geographical similarities.

There is another type of pattern of smaller, dispersed individual areas with an excessive number of low-income families situated within broader regions. These include parts of the northern Great Plains, scattered areas in the West and Pacific Northwest and, most extensive, areas on the piedmonts and the coastal plains in the Southeast. Here the difficulties seem attributable to causes other than those directly related to resource availability.

THE GREAT LAKES CUT-OVER

"Cut-over" is a harsh American phrase that describes a concentration of once forested land on the American shores of Lake Superior, Lake Michigan, and Lake Huron. Before settlement, the Great Lakes borderland was an area covered with cool northern evergreen forests on recent glacial till overlying the granitic base of the continent. Old mountain ranges rose above glacial ponds and lakes; winters were cold and long, not unlike those of Scandinavia. The Cut-over is a land of physical exploitation. First the original forest was cut down for lumber which found ready sale in the great Midwest agricultural plains; this region farther south was being settled at that same time and lumber for towns and farms was required. Following the lumber harvest, iron ore in great amounts was discovered in the region. Later, with the great industrial expansion, came the demand for high-grade ores which came from the deep mines of northern Michigan and Wisconsin and still later from the great open mines of northeastern Minnesota. The ores were taken by train to the lakeside terminals, and then by specially designed freighters to the steel mills on the shores of the Great Lakes at Chicago, northern Indiana, and Cleveland for direct smelting to iron and steel. Settlement was mainly in towns near the iron mines or on isolated farms where dairying and cool-weather crops were the rule. The area was prosperous during the period from 1890 to 1940 when its mines and forests supplied the insatiable demand for lumber and iron ore.

Conditions in the Cut-over region have changed. The remaining inferior ores must compete with new sources in Canada, Africa, and Latin America. New processes for pelletizing or concentrating the ores have dramatically shown the way to prolong the mining process—but probably at lower employment levels. The big timber harvest is finished; woods industries will be limited to specialized woods or new timber from more expensive reforestation. The poor soils, short growing season, and long shipping distances are not suitable for other than highly specialized agriculture. The many small, poor farms carved out of the woodland cannot compete with the highly mechanized dairy farms farther south. Therefore, agriculture cannot replace the high cash incomes of those formerly employed in mining and forestry. Unemployment in the area is twice the national average, with one man in four unemployed in some counties. Some workers have solved their problems by moving elsewhere; and new entrants to the labor force are employed at lower wages or also go elsewhere for work.

Interestingly, the area's responsible leaders are not content to adjust to unemployment in mining and forestry by simply removing themselves, their families, and their resources. Working together, through their institutions, they are exploring every possible alternative to removal. Their efforts are to develop new specialized industries based on unused resources, by improving the efficiency of the vital transportation systems, by retraining workers to new jobs, by exploiting the natural beauty of the wilderness for city vacationers. They are exploring every possible avenue of change and adjustment. Success (if one considers such adjustment to be a success) will depend on whether or not the residents prefer to work and wait for those adjustments or decide to move to new employment outside the area.

THE SOUTHEAST

The dispersed pattern of the rural poor in the Southeast is a distinct contrast to the tightly-knit regional concentration of the northern Cut-over. Here a broad region with a long, vital, and sometimes catastrophic common history has rich and productive soils, a permissive climate, and complex social and economic institutions.

Poverty is pervasive but noninclusive. Rich and poor divide resources in gravely disparate shares. The rich live among the poor. The poor have historically been a key element in an agriculture which is rooted in plantation origins.

Most influential is the historical predominance of single cash crop agriculture. This has produced a highly distinctive regional economy within the national economy—a system of producing, distributing, and consuming food, shelter, clothing, and services that is common to the region's inhabitants. Poverty is a direct residual of the maladjustments in this agricultural economy and its attendant cultural system, as it works out its changing relationships with the rest of the nation.

In this area are rich and varied soil types that provide the great potential for agricultural production. This potential is even greater because this area is located in the temperate and subtropical climate zones. In the Southeast are located about one third of America's agricultural land with a growing season of six months or over and nearly two thirds of the nation's area with an annual precipitation of 40 inches or more.

This is also an area of great forests where only fifteen years are required for a pine seedling to grow to pulpwood size. It is an area of great mineral resources, and an area of great potential water power; an area of prime location, close to ocean transport and not far separated from major population concentrations.

But there is a sharp contrast in wealth between the people who live in the South and those in other regions. In 1963, 32 per cent of the families in the South earned less than $3,000. This compared with 13 per cent in the Northeast, 17 per cent in the North Central, and 15 per cent in the West. Of the ten states in the United States with the lowest family income, nine are in the South. About half of all families in the United States earning less than $3,000 live in the South, and 60 per cent of these families earn less than $2,000.

Why does this area of great economic strength contain such a preponderance of poverty among the farm population? The answer lies in the single-crop system of agriculture in a region primarily suited to it. Cash crops have produced high returns per acre and per man-hour of labor. The direct consequence has been to keep down real income, that is, the value of all goods produced and sold plus those produced and consumed on the farms. It has lessened the pressure for diversification but lowered soil fertility. It has created a system of land tenure wherein a majority of farmers rent their farms and share the cash income from crops with the landowner. There has been little incentive to self-betterment, or to the development of firm attachment to the land, or for the promotion of farm husbandry. Estimates of damage due to soil erosion in the South on cash cropland reach 90 million acres. Some of this is due to friable soils and heavy rainfall, but poor farm practice has permitted it.

Low family income has meant inadequate expenditure for housing, nutrition, and health education. It has also meant inadequate sources of tax revenues for state and local governments and subsequently inadequate education facilities and teacher salaries, public health, and adequate investment in the infrastructure of a modern economic society in tune with other regions.

But after World War II pronounced changes in the South began to appear. The basic institutional and personal foundation is changing and there is not a single regional problem in the South that has not been subject to attack by local people aided in some degree by the federal government. Some of these are responses to conditions outside the South. Employment opportunities in northern cities offer an alternative to low-wage Southern agriculture. Changes in agricultural practice, employment opportunities in the South off the farms (stimulated by investment from without the area seeking to capitalize on wage differentials and other industrial advantages in these locations), positive and directed federal legislation in education and training, civil rights, health and farm extension training—all are acting to change the basis for local employment and opportunity.

109

REACTION TO REGIONAL POVERTY

Poverty does not fit the American ideal. But only within the past thirty years has systematic attention been given to a comprehensive welfare system. The elements of that system are diverse. Sar Levitan, an American who writes pungently on welfare problems, identifies three types: cash aid to those outside the labor force; programs to aid those in the work force; and services and goods to the poor regardless of labor force status.

The American geographer will recognize a somewhat different classification. There are those welfare programs that are designed to modify the environment in which people work so as to improve the regional efficiency. There are other programs that are designed to improve the efficiency of members of a particular group of citizens within a given regional context.

The second session of the Eighty-eighth Congress of the United States passed two laws designed to modify the infrastructure of American regions so as to benefit the inhabitants of such regions. These are the Appalachian Regional Development Act of 1964 and the Public Works and Economic Development Act. The preambles of these enactments acknowledge the deficiencies of certain regions in the United States and propose that careful plans be drawn to eliminate these deficiencies. They proposed that federal appropriation be made to discover unused resources for investment in new facilities which will improve the efficiency of the region and thereby provide new employment and increased family income. This is not the first time that such an experiment has been tried. An earlier attempt to modify the infrastructure of an American region, the Tennessee Valley Authority, succeeded in a striking way. Power and water development within an isolated major river valley brought new income to the area and significantly changed human use of area resources. Similar experiments were proposed in other regions, but most failed in Congress. The new programs will provide an opportunity to apply techniques of analysis and programming which have been developed since the TVA trial. New understandings of regional economics, the computer's capacity for handling vast information on the flow of goods and resources, and the development of new planning ideas seem likely to bring permanent new recovery to those American regions such as the Great Lakes Cut-over.

Programs are also under way to help the poor whose poverty is unrelated to their environment. These are the poor who are concentrated in city slums and the poor who experience the dispersed poverty of the Southeast and other rural areas.

Civil rights programs to combat racial discrimination, carefully directed tax programs, distribution of surplus foods, old-age insurance, direct aid to slum families, improved training and retraining of workers, assistance to the aged and the disabled, expanded educational opportunities, and improved job opportunities for youth are representative of such programs. These personal aids will improve the ability of individuals who find difficulty adjusting to the conditions in which they live.

America is wealthy enough to supplement the income of every citizen who does not have the minimum income necessary to represent a fair share of the nation's wealth. About 11 billion dollars a year would be necessary. This is less than 2 per cent of the total productivity of the nation.

But such a solution would satisfy neither the beneficiaries of such aid nor the benefactors who provided it. It would not provide a basis for a permanent solution directed to causes rather than symptoms. Success will require a serious pursuit of the causes of regional poverty which are unique and special to the areas in which they occur.

SUGGESTED READINGS

Harrington, M., *The Other America: Poverty in the United States.* New York: Macmillan, 1962.

Lansing, John B., and Barth, Nancy, *The Geographic Mobility of Labor: A Summary Report.* Area Redevelopment Administration. Washington, D.C.: Government Printing Office, 1964.

Levitan, Sar A., *Federal Aid to Depressed Areas: An Evaluation of the Area Redevelopment Administration.* Baltimore: Johns Hopkins Press, 1964.

Miller, Herman P., *Rich Man, Poor Man.* New York: Crowell, 1964.

Vernon, Raymond, *The Changing Economic Function of the Central City.* New York: Committee on Economic Development, 1959.

U. S. Bureau of the Census, *Census of Population: 1960; The Eighteenth Decennial Census of the United States.* Washington, D.C.: Government Printing Office, 1961.

U. S. Bureau of the Census. *Economic Development Act* (87–27), Eighty-seventh Congress. Senate Bill No. 1. Washington, D.C.: Government Printing Office, 1960.

U. S. Bureau of the Census, *The Economic Report of the President to the Congress.* Washington, D.C.: Government Printing Office, 1964.

U. S. Bureau of the Census, *Poverty in the United States,* Committee on Education and Labor, U. S. House of Representatives (committee print). Washington, D.C.: Government Printing Office, 1964.

9 AMERICA'S COASTAL AND OFFSHORE WATERS: USE PROBLEMS AND POTENTIALS

Lewis M. Alexander

Unique among all modern national states is the United States which plays a role as both a major land and a maritime power. Far from constituting a "lifeless" inchoate waste zone which separates America from its extra-continental neighbors, the sea serves as a living and complex bridge to the outside world. Technology and need have cast both coastal and offshore waters in new dimensions, and the "margins" of America are today not marginal but central to our thinking.

Facing on four major water bodies—the Atlantic Ocean, the Gulf of Mexico, and the Pacific and Arctic oceans—the marginal seas are important to the United States because of their various resources, their use by coastwise and foreign shipping, and their defensive depth role against attack from overseas. A geographer's concern with the sea areas adjoining the United States includes four elements: the nature of the coastline, the depths of the seabed, the extent of control claimed by government over marginal seas, and the uses which are made of these sea areas.

The coastline of the United States is over 11,000 miles in length (the Pacific Coast is by far the longest), of which just over half is in Alaska, 40 per cent is in "continental" United States, and 5 per cent in Hawaii. The physical nature of the coast varies considerably. Maine and southeastern Alaska have extremely rugged shorelines with many indentations and offshore islands and rocks. The Atlantic coast south of Boston, as well as the coast along the Gulf of Mexico, tends to be less irregular and is fringed with dunes and offshore sand barriers. Parts of the east coast have been "drowned" as evidenced by such indentations as Delaware and Chesapeake bays. Along the Gulf coast, the sand fringe is broken by the expanse of the Mississippi delta. Most of the.west coast, between Mexico and Canada, consists of headlands, with few bays or harbors. Western Alaska alternates between mountains and low-lying areas along its coast, while northern Alaska is lowland. The Hawaiian Islands are volcanic in origin and here again there are headlands, with coral reefs offshore.

While offshore islands play a significantly lesser role than do continental masses, they are of some consequence. Such islands include, in the Pacific, the Aleutian chain and the Alexander Archipelago of southeastern Alaska, as well as Santa Catalina and its neighboring islands off southern California. In the Atlantic, there are many small islands along the Maine coast; Nantucket, Martha's Vineyard, and Block Island on southeastern New England; and Long Island to the east of New York. Off southern Florida are three island groups: the Florida Keys; the British-held Bahamas; and Cuba, ninety miles to the south of Key West.

The nature of the United States coastline is important first because of its relationship to the "marine orientation" of the coastal inhabitants and second because of its use as a base for measuring zones of national jurisdiction in offshore waters. "Marine orientation" refers to the attitudes coastal peoples have toward the sea, the use they make of its resources, and their marine investments in terms of capital, education and training, and legislative controls. Some coastal communities are closely oriented toward the sea for such activities as fishing, recreation, or shipping. Other communities, in effect, "turn their back" on the adjacent waters and direct their attention toward the land. There is no simple relationship to be found between the physical nature of a coastline and the type of marine orientation existing there. But access to the sea, and from the coast into the interior, has often been an important element in terms of marine orientation. Along the rugged coasts of New England, for example, people early turned to the sea, developing fishing and shipping activities and building forts for defensive purposes. Recreation uses later became important, at a time when shipping began to be concentrated in a few large ports. Many of Alaska's inlets and offshore islands still support an important fishing economy, but some of these may in time change over to recreation, as in the past did such areas as Nantucket, the Bahamas, and Catalina Island. Sand beaches along the Atlantic and Gulf coasts have been taken over by vacationists who make use of the coastal waters. The military is also here, as evidenced by Cape Kennedy, and there are tidewater industries which have been attracted by low-cost water transport. Various coasts, then, offer particular opportunities for marine resource use—in the form of sandy beaches, natural harbors, rocky headlands, proximity to rich fishing grounds, or adjacency to empty ocean space. How the inhabitants of the coast avail themselves of these opportunities depends largely on prevailing attitudes and economic interests. In assessing the use problems and potentials of America's marginal seas, one must be aware of variations in the coastal conditions, since man lives on the land, and from the land he goes out to make use of the sea.

The physical nature of the coastline also affects the measurement of the various offshore zones of control. The United States, in conformity with international law, recognizes certain classifications of waters along its coasts. Bays, harbors, and river mouths are classed as *inland waters,* over which the nation has absolute sovereignty. Beyond the inland waters is the *territorial sea,* over which the nation also has sovereignty, save for the right of innocent passage through territorial waters by foreign vessels. Within these territorial waters only nationals of the coastal state may fish.

Baselines, the lines which separate land from territorial waters, are not always easily determined and can create international complications. If the coast is a fairly straight one, the baseline follows the low-tide mark; from here the territorial sea extends seaward a distance of three nautical miles. But with irregular coasts, difficulties arise in determining the baseline's position. In the case of a bay, for example, the baseline would not follow the indentations of the shoreline; rather it would be drawn as a straight line, up to a maximum length of twenty-four miles across the mouth of the bay. Each island has its own territorial sea, although in the case of islands less than six miles apart from one another or from the mainland, the adjoining territorial waters may coalesce with one another. Straight baselines are drawn across the mouths of rivers, again separating inland waters within the river from the territorial sea. Such practices illustrate the importance of coastal configuration to a nation's control of its offshore waters. Any extension of the baseline seaward of the low-tide line along the coast means a seaward extention of the limits of the territorial sea, as well as of the *contiguous zone*. This zone extends from the seaward limits of the territorial sea out to a distance of twelve miles from the shore. Within this three-to-twelve mile zone the United States claims the right to prevent violations of certain laws, such as those relating to smuggling and illegal immigration. Except for these preventive rights, however, the nation seeks to exercise no control over the waters of its contiguous zone, and foreigners are free to fish there or to use it for all types of shipping. For our purposes, "coastal waters" will be taken as those out to twelve miles from shore.

A most important physical characteristic of the United States coast is its *continental shelf*, the shallow underseas platform that slopes gradually seaward from the coastline. The outer edge of the shelf lies at a depth of some 600 feet; beyond this the seabed drops more steeply down to the ocean depths. The breadth of the continental shelf varies considerably off the United States, ranging from fewer than ten miles along parts of the California coast to 250 miles off northern Florida, and nearly 1,000 miles off the west coast of Alaska. The total area of the nation's continental shelf is over 800,000 square miles, of which two thirds is off Alaska.

In September, 1945, the President of the United States issued a proclamation extending the jurisdiction and control of the United States over the natural resources of the seabed and subsoil of the continental shelf, but without affecting the status of the waters above the shelf. Subsequent agreements at the 1958 Geneva Conference on the Law of the Sea confirmed all coastal nations' rights to control of the minerals of their continental shelf, as well as those marine organisms beyond territorial waters, which are "sedentary," that is, immobile on the floor of the shelf or able to move only in constant physical contact with the seabed. Such organisms include clams, oysters, and mussels, but not lobsters. One important asset of the shelf is that here are found most of the demersal, or bottom-feeding fish, such as cod, haddock, and flounder, which are valuable food fish.

If we accept the term "offshore waters" to refer to those sea areas beyond the twelve-mile "coastal" limit, out to a distance of some 300 miles from shore, then parts of America's "offshore" waters are underlain by the shelf, while other areas are truly "deep-sea" in character.

Not only external but also internal considerations play on the question of use rights of these coastal waters. Within the United States a bitter dispute arose some years ago over the rights of the federal government and the individual states concerning the resources in and beneath the coastal waters. The Submerged Lands Act of 1953 granted title to the states to all lands beneath navigable waters within their boundaries—that is, out to the three-mile territorial limit. Off the coasts of Texas and western Florida, this title extends to a distance of 10½ miles, because of special circumstances under which these states were admitted to the Union. Petroleum and other resources of the shelf belong to the individual states. But beyond the state boundaries the federal government has jurisdiction over the resources of the shelf, a distinction which are "sedentary," that is, immobile on the floor of the shelf companies for drilling purposes.

Of uses made of the coastal and offshore areas the two most important economically are fishing and petroleum extraction. The commercial fishing catch in the United States is valued at $400 million per year, and over 100,000 full-time fishermen are employed by the industry. The bulk of the catch comes from the coastal and offshore waters, although American-based shrimp boats range through the Caribbean to the South American coasts, tuna fleets fish the western Pacific down to Ecuador and Peru, while closer to home American fishermen work off Canada's east and west coasts.

There are five principal fishing areas off the United States. The New England area provides haddock, cod, whiting, and ocean perch from the Grand and Sable Banks off Canada, or Georges Bank off Cape Cod. Shellfish are also important, particularly clams and lobsters. In recent years, large numbers of Soviet trawlers have appeared off the New England coasts, beyond the three-mile territorial limit.

The Middle Atlantic area, from New York to Key West, provides menhaden, an industrial fish which is processed for oil, fertilizer, or animal feed, and oysters are particularly valuable in the Chesapeake Bay area. In the Gulf of Mexico, shrimp is the leading catch. In the Pacific, off California, tuna and sardines are the predominant species. From San Diego, the tuna fleet journeys south for thousands of miles along the west coast of the Americas.

The fifth, and most important of United States fishing areas, is the Northeast Pacific, from which come salmon, halibut, and king crab. Fishermen in American offshore waters often meet Japanese, Russian, and Canadian vessels, and several decades ago there was danger of depletion of the halibut, due to overfishing. By international agreement, the halibut fisheries are now restricted, a situation which also exists with respect to the fur seals of the Pribilof Islands off Alaska.

Three problems are important with regard to America's fishing industry. The first is the problem of conservation beyond territorial limits. With the increase in world-wide fishing effort and in fishing techniques, there is growing danger that particular species of fish may in time disappear completely. One means of protecting against overfishing by either Americans or foreigners would be for the government to extend the limits of its offshore control to the edge of the continental shelf. But the inclusion of all waters overlying the shelf within American jurisdiction would raise serious problems of international law. The United States is a party to several international fisheries commissions, such as those for the Northwest Atlantic and North Pacific fisheries and the Pacific Halibut and Salmon Fisheries Commissions. But such organizations cannot force member countries to restrict their fishing efforts. In addition, it is generally impossible for United States fishermen to assert their special rights to the fisheries immediately off their own coasts; rather, any conservation measure adopted to protect a particular species must be adhered to equally by fishermen of all nations. In view of the enormous catches being made by the Russians in recent years off the New England coast, it is possible that in time the Northwest Atlantic Commission may advise a general reduction in fishing effort for a period of time. But such a reduction would probably apply equally to both American and Soviet fishermen.

Associated with this is the problem of American fishing off foreign coasts, particularly Canada. The Canadian government is interested in closing off the Gulf of St. Lawrence to foreign fishermen and extending its exclusive fishing limits from three to twelve miles offshore, thereby challenging "historic" rights of American fishermen in Canadian coastal waters. To the south, United States fishermen must stay nine miles off the coasts of Mexico and are subject to arrest and fines if they go within two hundred miles of the coasts of Ecuador and Peru. For political reasons, they must also stay well clear of Cuban waters.

Beyond the question of fisheries control is that of the future of the American fishing industry itself. Although the total catch of nations such as Japan, Peru, and the Soviet Union has grown rapidly in recent years, that of the United States has shown little advance. There has been relatively little investment in modern ships and equipment, and the number of full-time fishermen has declined gradually since World War II. The value of fish imported into the United States is greater than that of the American catch. Unlike the American farmer, the fisherman does not receive subsidies for his product, and most of the equipment and techniques expended in commercial fishing have not changed substantially in the past thirty years. Technology and investment capital, which have done so much to transform the American economy within the past several decades, have to date had little effect on the commercial fishing industry.

The situation is completely different in the petroleum industry. The rate of capital investment in offshore drilling exceeds $1 million a day, and hundreds of wells are now operating on the continental shelf. Off the Louisiana coast is the most important producing area, whence comes about 6 per cent of the nation's annual petroleum production. A smaller producing area lies off southern California, and producing wells have recently been brought in off the Texas coast. In addition, exploratory work is under way off western Florida, Oregon and Washington, and in Cook Inlet, Alaska. It has been estimated that the petroleum resources beneath the continental shelf are equal to one third of the nation's próved reserves.

Sulphur, another important subsurface mineral, is recovered from coastal waters off Louisiana and Florida. As in the case of petroleum, boundary locations are important: first with respect to boundaries between areas of the seabed to which the states and the federal government hold title; and second between United States and Mexican territories in the Gulf of Mexico.

In addition to various minerals extracted from the sea water, such as sodium and potassium chloride, magnesium metal, and bromine, the marginal seas are important as disposal areas for sewage and industrial wastes; indeed, the problem of pollution of coastal waters has in some areas become critical. Not only are polluted waters injurious to the recreation industry, but also to fishing, particularly shellfishing. Clams and other shellfish have the capacity of concentrating pollutants within their body over a period of time, and contaminated shellfish may bring on epidemics of infectious hepatitis and other diseases.

Although pollution in inshore areas may be dangerous, disposal of wastes well offshore is often highly effective. Enteric bacteria experience a rapid die-off when discharged into salt water, and, if there is sufficient movement of salt water, adequate dilution of polluted materials is possible. Disposal of primary effluent into the ocean is a process approved by the Department of Health, Education and Welfare. On the other hand, disposal of radioactive wastes into the ocean could in time lead to dangerous concentrations, particularly along certain shore areas.

Use of the marginal seas for coastwise and foreign shipping requires constant improvement of coastal navigation facilities. Along the eastern seaboard is the intercoastal waterway, along which moves petroleum from Gulf ports to the Northeast, and coal from Hampton Roads to New England. Considerable cargo is carried via the Panama Canal between the East and West coasts, and trade also moves from Alaska and Hawaii to West coast ports. Finally, there are some 300 million tons of shipping annually entering United States ports which are engaged in trade between the United States and foreign countries.

Despite the radical innovations in types and uses of armaments, coastal and offshore waters remain important as defense zones to American strategy. American ships and planes during World War II were engaged in constant warfare against enemy submarines, and following the war a series of "Texas Towers" were erected off the coasts to assist in defense measures. These have been superseded by a system of hydrophones placed on the continental shelf, which can pick up the sound of approaching submarines several hundred miles off the coast and quickly determine their location. This network is augmented by continual air and sea patrols, and by warning systems against air attack. The defense of its offshore waters has long been a basic tenet of American policy, and while technology has radically altered the tactic of this defense, the aims of the policy remain the same.

In coming years there may be considerable increase in America's use of its marginal seas. Fisheries resources are known to exist which have only begun to be harvested—anchovies, hake, and mackerel off California, ocean perch off Alaska, and tuna in the Atlantic. On the shelf off Alaska are sands rich in iron and chromite, while titanium sands have been found off the Florida coast. In the ocean depths, beyond the shelf, are manganese and phospherite nodules, capable of being recovered. Use of the waters for recreation will certainly grow, as will also their use for shipping and as a disposal area.

The seas and oceans of the world have come to be referred to as the earth's "last frontier" awaiting development. In the United States, oceanographers, engineers, and other specialists are conscious of the new dimensions which have been opened up in the sea through recent advances in technology. A vast storehouse of resources await development in America's coastal and offshore waters—resources which can prove of value not only to the nation itself but to millions of people in the hungry world overseas as well.

SUGGESTED READINGS

Christy, F. T., and Scott, A., *The Common Wealth in Ocean Fisheries.* Baltimore: Johns Hopkins Press, 1965.

Pearcy, G. E., "Measurement of the U.S. Territorial Sea." *The Department of State Bulletin,* June 29, 1959, 1–10.

Reiff, H., *The United States and the Treaty Law of the Sea.* Minneapolis, Minn.: University of Minnesota Press, 1959.

Shalowitz, A. L., *Shore and Sea Boundaries.* 2 vols.; Washington, D.C.: U. S. Department of Commerce, Coast and Geodetic Survey, 1962.

10 GEOGRAPHICAL PREDICTION AND THEORY: THE MEASURE OF RECREATION BENEFITS IN THE MERAMEC BASIN

Edward L. Ullman

Prediction, as opposed to guessing or mere description, is the goal of science. Logical understanding may be a sufficient goal for many, but by definition correct prediction is a contribution both to science and, by extension, to society. This chapter will present a method of geographical prediction based on a combination of comparative or analog and interaction approaches. It will be applied to a difficult subject, the measurement of recreation benefits, an intangible item difficult to measure. Geographical prediction will be demonstrated, therefore, by a real problem in a real place, using real data to produce a real answer. This procedure can logically develop out of geographical thought.

RECENT STAGES IN GEOGRAPHIC THOUGHT

Before demonstrating the case, let us consider the recent history of geography. Geography has been preeminently a descriptive science and has hardly attempted prediction—much though we need to do this, and much though it is possible.

The recent history of geography in America may be divided

very roughly as follows into three overlapping periods: 1900 to 1920, 1920 to 1945, and 1945 to the present. The first stage emphasized the relations between man and his environment. This was essentially a neo-Darwinian reflection in geography, just as occurred in other fields. It was criticized as being too deterministic—of making too much of the environment, of overasserting and oversimplifying environmental controls over man's action.

As a reaction to this environmental determinism, a second general approach developed—overlapping the first stage—from roughly 1920 to 1940 or 1945. This new emphasis actually went back to an even earlier conception of geography, essentially more descriptive, but emphasizing the *differences* from place to place and was eloquently and exhaustively documented in Richard Hartshorne's justly famous *The Nature of Geography* (Washington, D.C.: Association of American Geographers, 1937). A shorthand way of describing geography then was to define it as the science of *areal differentiation*. That stage coincided particularly with regional approaches and regional descriptions. Some critics remarked that if the previous period had been deterministic, this second period might be even worse, since it was nihilistic, and nihilism was scarcely an advance over determinism!

CHARACTERISTICS OF THE PRESENT STAGE OF GEOGRAPHICAL THOUGHT

From about 1940 or 1945 or even later, we come into the present period. While it is difficult to define this stage because we are in the midst of it, from the written and unwritten record today and since the war, there appear to be six characteristics of the present period differentiating it—though not altogether—from the earlier ones. These six characteristics of modern geography, particularly in America, follow in a somewhat chronological order.

1. Increased emphasis on the topical or systematic. This means delving into a topical subject such as transportation or manufacturing or agriculture, rather than trying to cover everything. This allows for deeper penetration. This emphasis was given particular publicity by Edward Ackerman's publication in the *Annals of the Association of American Geographers*, "Geographic Training, War Time Research and Immediate Professional Objectives," at the end of the war in which he recounted the lessons of geographers' wartime experiences. Geographers, paradoxically, during the war, had argued for a systematic or topical division of knowledge rather than a regional one, as did many of the other social scientists.

2. Inherited from earlier periods is the genetic or historical approach. Still of primary concern with many geographers, the genetic approach is not characteristic of this research, though similarities may be seen—since the genetic approach does often involve problem solving, process, and diffusion or interaction.

3. A very important, substantive characteristic of the present period may be characterized as the functional or interaction approach. This includes circulation, interaction, transportation, communication—a geography of movement, as opposed to a static geography. Much work is being done in this field in various forms. Transportation is peculiarly a geographic subject; it is the device for overcoming space, and space is of the essence in geography. Some years ago, Professor Harold McCarty of the University of Iowa and Professor Richard Hartshorne of the University of Wisconsin presented views at the Santa Monica meeting of the Association of American Geographers. McCarty spoke of a geography of production; Hartshorne, quoting André Allix, for a geography of consumption. Afterwards, it came to me that really much better than either of their suggestions would have been a geography of circulation or transportation. The *connection* between production and consumption is peculiarly geographical.

Whatever is or is not peculiarly geographical, we are most interested in whether or not these new trends can produce an approach which pays off. However, we are also interested in whether or not the approach justifies geography as a separate, but related, discipline.

4. An increased, in fact new, emphasis on quantitative approaches. By this is meant measurement, both inductive and deductive, and the use of statistics and mathematical models. This is a characteristic of all sciences, and a characteristic of our age. Geography is also pursuing this method; in order to predict, it is important to be able to put data into quantitative terms for manipulation. This is not to assert, however, that the quantitative approach is everything. It is no substitute for ideas, concepts, or empirical data. It is, in all cases, a tool, and properly used helps to produce substantive findings and theory.

5. An emphasis on theory, which might be broken down into simple concepts and systems or general order. These last three characteristics—the interaction approach, the quantitative approach, and the theoretical approach—often are tied together.

6. Finally—and our main point—application and prediction. We will show, by the operation of an actual prediction model applied to a region, examples of the use of five of the trends: topical, functional or interaction, quantitative, theoretical, and predictive.

Still other trends may be emerging. For example, there is considerable evidence for the value of (1) a perception-behavior assessment often of irrational activities affecting space, and (2) an artistic-amenity appreciation of landscape. The first trend may well reflect a heightened psychological-social concern in America, and the second a rising concern with esthetics and amenity, in an increasingly affluent and educated society which values both urban design and natural beauty. These approaches will not be discussed further here, but the writings of Wolpert on the first, and Lowenthal and the magazine *Landscape,* edited by J. B. Jackson, on the second, are illustrative. These approaches, especially the second, also are reflected somewhat in the amenity goals of the Meramec Project.[1]

DEFINING GEOGRAPHY

These trends can also be reflected in a new, partial definition of geography; one pointed toward geography as spatial interaction:

The goal of geography is the codification of relations between objects—occupance units—in earth space. Attention is focused on economic or social relations promoting tangible interchange as measured by flow of goods or people, trade areas, or regional groupings, but not excluding movement of ideas.

The basic assumptions are: (1) the closer things are in space the closer are their relations, or (2) that there are definite categories of spatial relations not following the proximity rule, but exhibiting degrees of interconnection in response to varying degrees of spatial complementarity and mobility. They fall into patterns of contiguous or non-contiguous diffusion, into corridors of interaction, into waves, or other manifestations of varying degrees of intensity and order, and into relations between separated nuclei of differing hierarchical or other characteristics.

Codification of these spatial relations into tendencies for understanding or laws in order to predict is the goal of scientific geography. The imaginative application of these spatial procedures and theories to a range of practical and social problems is the justification for applied geography.

[1] For calling my attention to these and some other points, I am indebted to Harold Brodsky.

THE MERAMEC BASIN STUDY
AS A PREDICTION MODEL

The setting is the Meramec River Basin, in the American Middle West, a river basin about one hundred by fifty miles extending from the St. Louis suburbs in Missouri down into the Ozark Mountains. I was asked to conduct a study of the region for the purpose of general economic development, but with particular reference to water resources and flood protection—in other words, a specialized regional planning study.

The area is heavily forested, rough, mostly plateau surface and is one of the emptiest areas in terms of population in the eastern half of the United States, resembling the Adirondacks or the upper peninsula of Michigan; yet it is only fifty miles from a metropolitan area of 2 million persons. This immediately suggests, without any elaborate models or statistical preparation, a recreational relation between the metropolitan area and this wilderness area.

Probably few cities in the country are farther from suitable water recreation than St. Louis. Therefore, we began to wonder whether the rapid increase in demand for recreation and the change in technology now warranted building, in a sense, an "ocean" nearby. In other words, the market appears equally important, if not more important in many cases, than natural features in the geography of the twentieth century. Figure 10–1 shows visitors at the eight large reservoirs in the St. Louis universe, with pie-shaped sectors indicating estimated visitors from St. Louis.

The problem was to estimate how much benefit would result from providing a large lake for recreation. The costs could be readily figured, but estimating the benefits was an unsolved problem. Benefits of course should exceed the costs. This is the classic

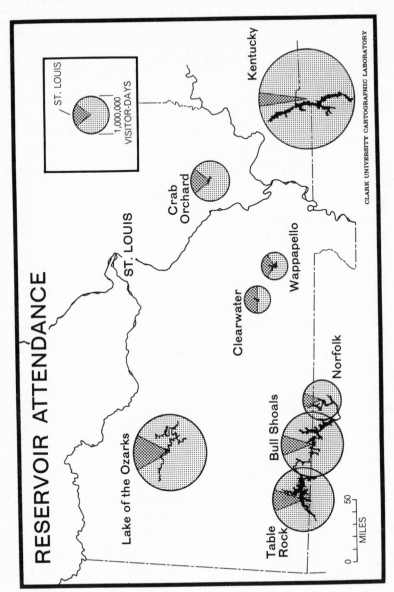

RESERVOIR ATTENDANCE

ST. LOUIS

1,000,000 VISITOR-DAYS

ST. LOUIS

Lake of the Ozarks

Crab Orchard

Clearwater

Wappapello

Table Rock

Bull Shoals

Norfolk

Kentucky

0   50
MILES

CLARK UNIVERSITY CARTOGRAPHIC LABORATORY

Figure 10–1

way in which American water resource problems are investigated, and indeed, the same procedure is being tried on other problems. Recreation as noted, however, is an intangible item, difficult to measure. In fact, economists had formerly thrown up their hands at the problem but, rushing in where angels feared to tread, we did invent a method for measuring the benefits of recreation.[2]

The method invented illustrates what is called here *geographical prediction*. The term is employed in a very specific way. Normally, one might say there is only one kind of prediction—achieved simply by measuring a trend, such as population increase per decade, and projecting this trend into the future. Thus, most valid prediction is an adjusted projection of an existing trend. This might be termed *historical prediction*.

But what does one do when there is no trend to project—when building something new, for example. We needed to know (1) how many visitors would attend a new lake, and (2) what the number of visits were worth.

This calls for inventing a second method of prediction: *geographical prediction*. This means that if one has no trend to project in the particular area, one looks for essentially analogous conditions elsewhere, transfers that setting to the study area, making appropriate adjustments, and uses the results for prediction. This could also be called the *geographical analog* method. It is a natural by-product of comparative geography and one which can be used widely. The idea was first used by this author as a device for predicting traffic on a proposed railroad line in the Philippines in 1956.

In the operation of this particular prediction model, advantage was also taken of the quantitative approach by ordering the data into either a gravity model or simply a distance regression line. An interaction or functional approach was also employed: we

[2] This method, although developed independently, turned out to be related in varying degree to suggestions and work of Hotelling, Clawson, and others as noted below.

were interested in where people have gone. Our fundamental theory was that the number of visitors declines somewhat in proportion to distance—a version of the gravity model.

Step I: Estimating Attendance

Responsibility for implementing the model was shared with Professor Donald J. Volk, now of the University of Maryland, who in fact gathered and processed most of the data which follow. Data were obtained from the Missouri Conservation Commission on the origin of fishermen who had caught fish at many lakes in the state of Missouri. Altogether, there were 100,000 or more of these origins—which were fugitive data acquired merely as by-products of catching fish. Oftentimes more knowledge is available about fish than about people! We are fortunate to find these data; but one does not find data unless one knows what to look for—in other words, has a theory. If we had not found these data, we would have extended our own surveys to provide substitute data.

The origins of fishermen were plotted by counties and converted to per capita measures on maps. The number, in general, declined with distance. (See Figure 10-2: one of numerous maps for various reservoirs in the original report.) These data were also plotted on a scatter diagram with logarithmic scales (Figure 10-3).

On the average, the decline in attendance was proportionate to distance to the third power, indicating a rather rapid decline in attendance with distance. This indicates further that one reservoir or lake is probably more or less substitutable for another, and therefore the fishermen go to the nearer impoundments. This contrasts to some of the unique natural features of the West, such as Yellowstone Park or Grand Canyon, where decline in attendance appears to be more gradual, resembling distance squared.

On the average, we found also that we tended to get somewhat

Lake of the Ozarks, Niangua Arm
INTENSITY OF USE BY FISHERMEN

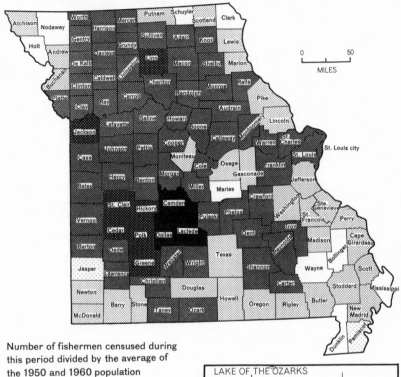

Number of fishermen censused during
this period divided by the average of
the 1950 and 1960 population

	.01 to .1
	.1 to 1
	1 to 10
	10 to 100
	100 to 1000

Source: Missouri Conservation Commission

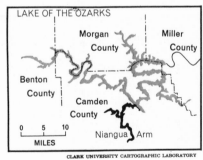

Ullman and Volk Meramec Basin Research Project

CLARK UNIVERSITY CARTOGRAPHIC LABORATORY

Figure 10–2

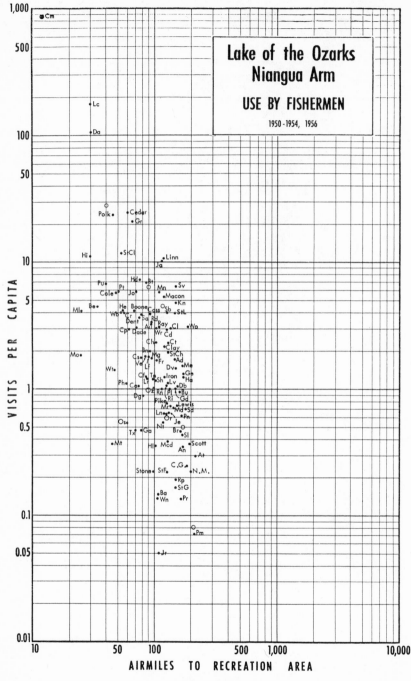

Figure 10-3

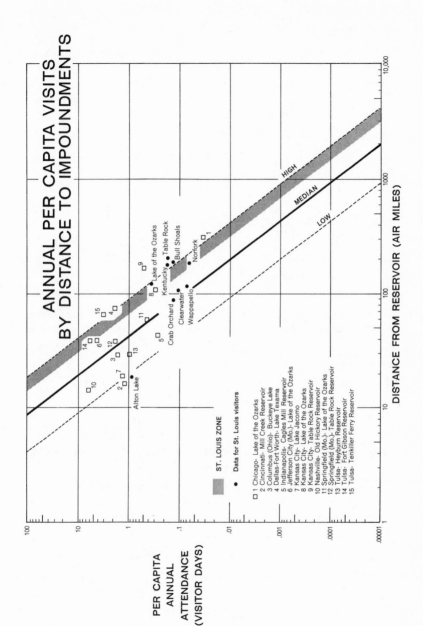

Figure 10–4

more visits from urban or high-income counties and less from lower-income counties or from counties in which there were intervening opportunities—that is another lake in-between. Three lines were therefore plotted on the graph, a median line, an urban high-income line, and a rural low-income line; this became our prediction model (Figure 10–4). From this, with some adjustments, we could predict attendance anywhere we put down a lake. We could read off a certain distance on the horizontal axis and find, for example, at fifty miles the visits from an urban high-income county would be four visits per capita per year.

This model was operated for a variety of locations around St. Louis, and tables made for each location simply by drawing circles of twenty-mile bands around each impoundment (Table 10–1), multiplying the population in the circular zone by the per capita attendance expected for that distance, to produce an estimate of the number of visitor-days per year. The biggest contributor in all these was the St. Louis metropolitan area with its 2 million people. For one hypothetical lake fifty miles from St. Louis (Table 10–1), this came out to 8 million visitor days per year from the St. Louis metropolitan area alone, which would mean the highest attendance at any reservoir in America. But this is no more than one might expect for a reservoir so near a large metropolis.

The prediction in this case was based on the attendance which would result from building a reservoir with the average characteristics of the large ones in our analog origins (Figure 10–1). As a check on our prediction model, we plotted attendance from a variety of cities in the country to nearby reservoirs for as many cities as we could obtain (Figure 10–4). The plots all fell on the lines of the graph more or less as expected. As a matter of fact, St. Louis visitor-days to five large impoundments from 100 to 125 miles away were all in the high zone in per capita attendance, whereas St. Louis visitor-days at three other smaller impoundments were in the median zone. Without exception those in the

TABLE 10–1. *Estimated Attendance at Hypothetical Major Impoundment 50 Air Line (60 Road) Miles from St. Louis.*

DISTANCE ZONES FROM HYPOTHETICAL RESERVOIR	POPULATION IN ZONE	PER CAPITA CATEGORY[a]	ANNUAL VISITS NUMBER	TOTAL ANNUAL VISITOR-DAYS
0–10	20,000	median	15+	300,000
10–20	40,000	median	10+	400,000
20–40	90,000	high	10+	900,000
40–60	2,000,000[b]	high	4	8,000,000
60–100	300,000	low	.4	120,000
100–200	2,000,000	median	.03	60,000
200–300	10,000,000	median	.005	50,000
300–500	30,000,000	median	.001	30,000
Beyond 500	(Rest of U.S.)	Estimate		50,000
			TOTAL	9,910,000

[a] Categories refer to per capita annual visits expected based on numerous origin surveys in 1960, at large impoundments in Missouri, Illinois, and Kentucky. *High* refers to per capita expectation from urban, high-income, and/or lack of intervening opportunities for recreation at nearer impoundments; *low* refers to rural, low-income, and/or intervening opportunities for recreation at closer impoundments. *Median* is average between two extremes.

[b] Includes most of St. Louis metropolitan area.

high zone were the better and larger impoundments and those in the median zone were poorer and smaller impoundments. This variation in the expected direction made us feel that the prediction was reasonably valid.

Although we acquired more meaningful quantitative data on origins and other characteristics than any previous study, certain inherent defects of the data make untenable more precise calculations, such as the correlation coefficient of the slope of attendance decline by distance, etc. Furthermore, estimates of total attendance at reservoirs, although checked in various ways, did vary. Not the least of our problems was the definition of a "visitor-day," since attendance can range from a ten-minute stop to view a dam, to an all-day picnic or fishing expedition. For this reason, in many of our actual calculations in the Meramec study, we arbitrarily cut the visitor-day estimates in half and made other adjustments. For the purposes of Table 10–1, however, we have not done this so that the figures can be compared nationally.

The predictions based on fishermen were checked with some other data and were related to total attendance at reservoirs. From other surveys we found that fishermen's travel patterns, especially in the fifty-mile range, were very like the average travel patterns for most other major purposes. Of course, the precise behavior of fishermen is unpredictable; in some years some lakes put out more fish, others less, and this affects fishermen's destinations. All we were attempting to establish was the average situation over a period of years. For planning purposes, we made extrapolations over the usual fifty-year period, discounted at stated per cents, and for a four- or fivefold increase reflecting increased affluence and population.

Step II: Estimating Benefits

In addition to attendance, we needed to know what these visitor-days were worth. This was estimated in two ways: first, by a primitive diversion model; and second, by a generated and diverted visitor model.

The Diversion Model

As a first approximation, a diversion model was devised, based on how many St. Louis visitor-days might be diverted from the eight impoundments in the St. Louis universe, lakes ranging from 100 to 125 miles away, by building a lake only 50 miles away. The diversion was estimated on the basis of surveys made at various Missouri State Parks based on the question: "If a lake similar to this one were built half as far away from your home, would this decrease your visits to this lake to the extent of eliminating completely, reduce greatly, reduce slightly, no effect, don't know?" The responses were arbitrarily scored 100 per cent, 75 per cent, 25 per cent, zero, and the last, "don't know," responded by about 20 per cent, was allocated proportionately. The combined score of this rough-and-ready approximation indicated a diversion of about one-third of the existing visitors if a lake were built only 50 or 60 miles from St. Louis. This was a conservative figure; at first, we thought this a fortiore approach indicated more than enough potential benefit to justify construction. After working out some of the estimates, however, we found that the diversions alone did not give quite enough benefit, although the operation of this model gave somewhat of an independent check on the subsequent model.

Generated and Diverted Visitors: A Travel Savings Model

A more complete measure was needed to give the value of newly *generated* business as well as diverted business. How would one measure this generated business? This we were able to work out quite simply, in retrospect, from our attendance prediction model itself (Figure 10–4).

The rationale is as follows: if a reservoir were built 50 miles from St. Louis according to the graph (Figure 10–4), 8 million visitor-days would be willing to go 50 miles or farther, but 4,600,-000 of those would be willing to go 60 miles, 2,800,000 would go 70 miles, and so on (Table 10–2). These 4,600,000 visitors are in essence being given a gift of 10 miles. They are willing to pay to go 60 miles. But, if a new reservoir is provided only 50 miles away, each of them is given a gift of 10 miles, or a 20-mile round trip, etc.

The next problem was to figure out what these saved miles were worth. We did this by putting a value on them of about three cents per visitor-day mile, comprised half of modest estimates of vehicle out-of-pocket or variable operating costs—gasoline, oil, tires, etc., but not depreciation. The other half consisted of estimates of the value of time which were taken from standard American highway manuals and averaged with other estimates we had made.

Economists are often unhappy with estimates of the value of time. They query: "How do you know what the value of time is?" My first answer is, "I don't care." If we are wrong, by say 50 per cent, it still affects our total figure by only about 25 per cent plus or minus. Personally, I think the value of time on the average is more important in somebody's calculation than the value of gasoline and oil used on a trip.

This whole model applies to America where the automobile is overwhelmingly the vehicle used for this type of recreation. In other parts of the world, where buses and other vehicles are also used, this would not be so true but similar measures could be readily, in fact more easily made, by using actual fares paid.

Each ten-mile block (Columns 1, 2, and 3 in Table 10–2) is multiplied by the unit savings (Column 4) based on the following logarithmic block averages: 3 miles, 13, 23, 33, etc., and the savings are totaled in the last column (Column 5). We get a total savings of $4,728,000 in the blocks of visitors willing to go to an impoundment in this particular location. We then took the 8 million visitor-days (the theoretical total unadjusted attendance) and divided them into $4,728,000 to produce 59 cents per visitor-day which we rounded off to 60 cents. This was the actual figure we used in our visitor-day calculations—60 cents per visitor-day for benefits.

A value per visitor-day is a convention commonly used; we are not too happy with this convention, but the $4,728,000 can be used any way one wants. It represents a *net national* saving, and has the virtue of not having any double counting or other tricks in it.

TABLE 10–2. *Potential Travel Savings for Impoundment 50 Miles from St. Louis.*

DISTANCE FROM ST. LOUIS (AIR MILES)	VISITOR (DAYS) WILLING TO GO DISTANCE IN COL. 1, OR FARTHER[a]	APPROXIMATE VISITOR (DAYS) IN EACH INCREMENTAL TEN-MILE BLOCK	TRAVEL AND TIME CENTS PER VISITOR-DAY[b]	COST SAVING APPROXIMATE TOTAL (COL. 3 × 4)
1	2	3	4	5
50	8,000,000	3,400,000	9	$304,000
60	4,600,000	1,700,000	39	669,000
70	2,880,000	960,000	69	658,000
80	1,920,000	580,000	99	575,000
90	1,340,000	360,000	129	470,000
100	980,000	246,000	159	390,000
110	734,000	170,000	189	321,000
120	564,000	121,000	219	265,000
130	443,000	89,000	249	222,000
140	354,000	67,000	279	187,000
150	287,000	51,000	309	158,000
160	236,000	39,000	339	132,000
170	197,000	32,000	369	118,000
180	165,000	25,000	399	100,000
190	140,000	20,000	429	86,000
200	120,000	16,000	459	73,000
210	104,000			
			TOTAL	$4,728,000 ($.59 per visitor-day)

a Based on unadjusted figures in Table 1 for St. Louis visitor-days alone to impoundment.

b At $.03 per visitor-day mile x one-half round trip distance (represents round trips divided by two days, the average duration of trip as determined by survey at Meramec State Park).

This particular model, which might be called a "geographical analog, spatial interaction model," to use geographic language, is similar to the "travel savings version of a consumer's surplus model" from economics. Here geographic thinking and economic thinking meet in a common end.

The first to suggest this method in a preliminary way was Harold Hotelling, Professor of Statistics at the University of North Carolina, who apparently argued for giving everyone, regardless of distance traveled, as benefits, the cost incurred by the longest distance traveled.[3]

Trice and Wood actually operated a somewhat similar method in California, but based on a very small sample, to arrive at a figure of $2.00 per visitor-day.[4] They based this figure on the difference between the median distance traveled and almost the longest distance, the ninetieth percentile. This cut down the amount suggested by Hotelling, but presents no persuasive rationale for taking even this great a benefit. Subsequently, Marion Clawson developed the hypothesis systematically in 1959 and plugged in a few suggestive attendance data at National Parks. Subsequent work by J. L. Knetsch and others carried the methods further.

Optimum Admission Fee

One other way to use the data was to imagine that a fence would be built around the reservoir, a gate constructed, and admission charged—a classic economic solution. What admission fee would give the greatest return? This we were able to calculate (Figure 10–5). We found that about $1.00 would give the greatest gross return, $1.29 the greatest net return, if one postulates a reasonable 20 cents per visitor-day maintenance cost. There would be fewer visitors with a fee, of course, than if nothing were charged. Thus, we also solved this economic problem by use of a spatial or geographical approach.

[3] This suggestion was in a letter to the National Park Service shortly after World War II.

[4] A. H. Trice and S. E. Wood, "Measurement of Recreation Benefits," *Land Economics,* XXXIV, (August 1958), 195–207.

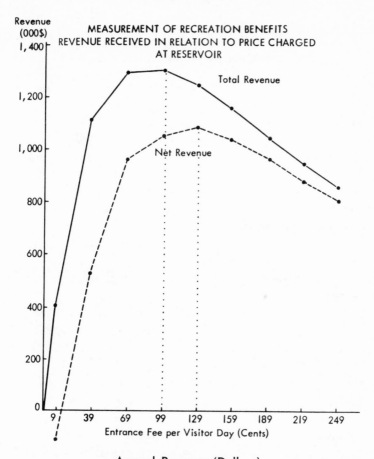

MEASUREMENT OF RECREATION BENEFITS
REVENUE RECEIVED IN RELATION TO PRICE CHARGED
AT RESERVOIR

Annual Revenue (Dollars)

Entrance Fee (Cents)	Number of St. Louis Visitor Days	Total	Net (Assuming 20 Cents per Visitor Day Maintenance)
0	8,000,000	0	−1,600,000
9	4,600,000	414,000	−106,000
39	2,880,000	1,123,200	547,000
69	1,920,000	1,324,800	940,800
99	1,340,000	1,326,660	1,058,600
129	980,000	1,264,200	1,088,200
159	734,000	1,167,060	1,021,000
189	564,000	1,064,210	951,460
219	443,000	970,170	881,570
249	354,000	881,460	800,660

Add c. 20 per cent for all visitors

Figure 10–5

Conclusion: What Creates an Idea?

This case of geographical prediction is presented because it does represent a breakthrough—an invention, if you please, which this author wishes to share. This brings up the question of the value of an applied job. Oftentimes an applied job is considered less desirable than a theoretical or academic approach. But many times the reverse can be true. It is true that "Leisure to experiment and reflect" is necessary, as Carl Sauer notes in speculating about the development of human learning "Environment and Culture during the Last Deglaciation." [5]

If one is forced to come up with an answer, however, one's head, so to speak, is pushed up against the wall. Sometimes an imaginary answer is given; sometimes a real answer can be invented.

This in turn brings up the question as to what does produce a creative idea? By no means do I know what fundamentally gives one an idea, but two or three conditions seem to be helpful: (1) *interaction* with somebody with a slightly different way of thinking or approach, and (2) *necessity*. This is the old saw of necessity being the mother of invention. Both these factors help one to produce an original idea and to make an original contribution, especially if enough time is also available to reflect and experiment. A gestation period appears to be necessary to develop the idea, followed by secondary breakthroughs, somewhat analogous to the stages in the firing of a rocket.

[5] *Proceedings of the American Philosophical Society*, XCII (1948), pp. 65–77.

SUGGESTED READINGS

Ackerman, E. A., "Geographic Training, War Time Research and Immediate Professional Objectives." *Annals of the Association of American Geographers,* XXXV (1945), 121–143.

Clawson, M., "Methods of Measuring the Demand for and Value of Outdoor Recreation." Reprint No. 10, *Resources for the Future.* Baltimore, Md: Johns Hopkins Press, 1959.

Hartshorne, R., *The Nature of Geography.* Washington, D.C.: Association of American Geographers, 1937.

Hartshorne, R., *Perspectives on the Nature of Geography.* Chicago, Rand McNally, 1959.

Knetsch, J. L., "Outdoor Recreation Demands and Benefits." *Land Economics,* XXXIX (November 1963).

Knetsch, J. L., "The Influence of Reservoir Projects on Land Values." *Journal of Farm Economics,* February 1964.

Sauer, C. O., *Land and Life.* John Leighly (ed.). Berkeley, University of California Press, 1963.

Ullman, E. I., "The Role of Transportation and the Bases for Interaction," in W. Thomas (ed.), *Man's Role in Changing the Face of the Earth.* Chicago: University of Chicago Press, 1956, pp. 862–880.

Ullman, E. L., Boyce, R., and Volk, D., *The Meramec Basin: Water and Economic Development.* St. Louis: Washington University Press and Meramec Basin Corporation, 1962.

Ullman, E. L., and Volk, D., "An Operational Model for Predicting Reservoir Attendance and Benefits." *Michigan Academy of Science, Arts and Letters,* XLVII (1962), 473–784.

11 THE UNITED STATES AND ITS GEOPOLITICAL SETTING

Saul B. Cohen

A nation's significance in world affairs changes with the quality and organization of its domestic resource base and its pattern of association, economic, political, and military, with other parts of the world. This change comes about not simply as a response to the objective environment, internal and external, but also to the perceived environment. With a constantly expanding economy based on accelerated increase in exploitation of domestic resources, and an expanded pattern of international associations, the United States by the end of World War II had become a great, self-contained power with economic and military access to most parts of the world. Its global location had now shifted from the eccentric one, which had been its characteristic until the end of the nineteenth century, to a central one. Revolutionary innovations in transportation and communication, immigration, military involvements and capabilities, ideological goals, and economic needs had combined to forge new patterns of global relations.

What was perhaps not widely understood during this period of America's entry into globalism was the delicate relationship between internal spatial change and external spatial association. Indeed, because these processes are never timed coincidentally, such understanding could not have been fully anticipated. Hindsight permits us now to grasp the full meaning of this relationship as reciprocal or mutual—not one caused solely by the response of the foreign to the domestic scene, or vice versa.

The impact of this new-found post-World War II setting on the American power, a *fact,* was misconstrued by many to mean that the role of the United States in world affairs in a highly egocentric fashion. That the sun did not set on the global arena of American power, a *fact,* was misconstrued by many to mean that the orbit of this American sun and its play on the earth were totally unrelated to the capacities and needs of other nations—a *fallacy.* Thus, for example, America's European allies and the Communist world alike were accepted as important, but nevertheless passive, agents in the unfolding pattern of American globalism. Junior partnership status for one, and containment for the other, were resultant policies. Moreover, the traditional primary role played by the United States in Latin America, and the post-World War II role taken up in offshore Asia, were being projected onto such new scenes as the Middle East, South and Southeast Asia, and Africa.

This was a time when the Franco-British role in the Middle East was clearly on the wane, and when American economic and military involvement was assuming larger proportions in South and Southeast Asia. It was also a time when traditional lines of orientation between Maritime Europe and Africa were being challenged by the rising expectations of African nationalism, by the stirring interest of Asian Communist and neutral nations in the African revolt against colonialism, and by the financial and ideological entry of the United States onto the African scene.

It was difficult then for many Americans to appreciate the resentment which many Europeans felt at the manner in which their United States ally appeared to be projecting its power and influence in Africa. When American leaders spoke to Africa, some tended to present themselves as deliverers from the ancient regime. Many Africans consequently assumed that the United States had both the ability and the willingness to establish a new era of trans-atlantic partnership that would wipe out the substantial achievement and heritage, good as well as bad, of African-European association. Recent events have shown, however, that the potential significance of the United States in Africa had been overplayed in many circles—that while important new forms of financial, military, and moral ties needed to be and were being forged, these could not completely substitute for or supplant the European presence in Africa, that they could only complement this presence. Most recently, the same condition has become more readily apparent in United States relations with parts of Asia, certainly the Middle East and South Asia. There are now substantially fewer people in the United States who wish, or believe, that Western responsibilities in these regions can or should become the sole responsibility of the United States.

Consider the ironic parallel of the past few years, when the traditional lines of orientation between the United States and Latin America were being changed by Latin American nationalism, when both Soviet and Chinese Communist penetration of Latin America added yeast to this process of fermentation, and when President Charles de Gaulle of France dramatically paid a personal visit to Latin America, seeking to forge new spiritual and economic lines between Europe and Latin America. The intensity of resentment expressed by some Americans against this foray in their "backyard" was very much like the previously mentioned European resentment of United States entry into Africa.

The word "entry" has been used to describe these postwar United States-African and European-Latin American links, and not intrusion. History, hopefully, will record the valued role of these links in unifying that part of the Maritime World that one day may emerge as the Atlantic community. Nevertheless, this trans-atlantic crisscross of orientation carries with it considerable misunderstanding and miscalculation stemming from overselling and overexpectation. Maritime Europe's increased ties with Latin America through the feeling of Latinité, the increase of technical assistance, and the broadening of trade lines cannot supplant the economic, strategic, and psychological ties that bind North and Latin America—they can only complement them. The same holds true for the primacy of Eurafrican lines within this framework.

The foregoing serves to introduce a discussion first of an American political geographer's view of his own country within its domestic and regional and then in its global setting. It is a discussion that arises from the continuing quest of the geographer to gain deeper insight into the distribution of national power, especially political and economic, over the earth's surface, and the changing patterns of this distribution. The problem of maintaining some degree of dynamic equilibrium or balance of the earth's contending political forces is not exclusively a political problem. It is interrelated with the economic, social, and technological fabric of the man-earth system. Hence we have spoken in previous works of geopolitical, not political, equilibrium, composed of competing regions of two ranks or orders. The basis for the system by which global equilibrium is maintained is that of a hierarchy or nesting for a world divided into major geostrategic regions, diverse geopolitical subregions, and other units. Where only a decade ago one spoke of single power cores (the United States and the Soviet Union), today one speaks of multiple power cores around which the world is geostrategically organized (Figure 11–1).

The *geostrategic region* must be large enough to possess global influencing characteristics and functions, because today's strategy can be expressed only in global terms. Essentially, such a region is the expression of the interrelationship of a large part of the world in terms of location, movement, trade orientation, and cultural or ideological bonds. While it is a single-feature region in the sense that its purpose is to embrace areas over which power can be strategically applied, the geostrategic is a multifeature region in its composition, because today's strategy has political-economic as well as military characteristics.

149

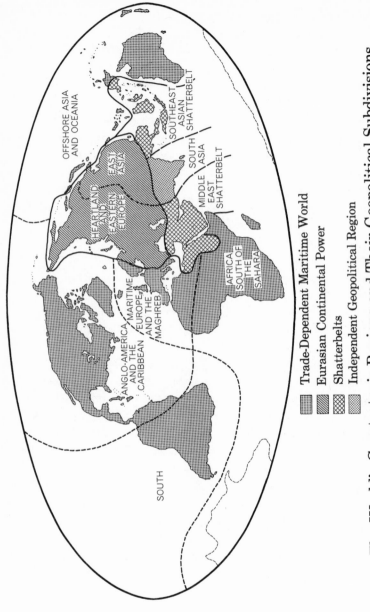

The World's Geostrategic Regions and Their Geopolitical Subdivisions

Figure 11–1

Legend:

■ Trade-Dependent Maritime World
▨ Eurasian Continental Power
▧ Shatterbelts
▩ Independent Geopolitical Region

The *geopolitical region* is a subdivision or subsystem of the above. Because it is derived closely from geographic regions, it can provide a framework for common political and economic actions. Contiguity, economic and social complementarity of resources, effective movement links, areas of intermediately dense populations which can absorb additional peoples, empty areas, historic association, and dominance of core areas are generally distinguishing features of the geopolitical region. Geopolitical regions are the basis for the emergence of multiple power nodes within a geostrategic region—a process which leads to complications owing to the overlap of interfaces. Thus a core area's dominance over the periphery of its geopolitical region can be weakened as that peripheral area strengthens its geostrategic ties with the core area of another geopolitical unit (for example, U.S.S.R.-Albanian-Chinese relations).

The *shatterbelt* is defined as a large, strategically located region that is occupied by a number of conflicting states and is caught between the conflicting interests of great powers in geostrategic regions that adjoin or have access to the region. Conflict of interests between geostrategic regional partners intensifies the complex nature of these shatterbelts.

The geostrategic region of which the United States is a part is termed the *Trade-Dependent Maritime Geostrategic Region* formed, binodally, around the Maritime Ring of the United States and the western European conurbation which extends from the Thames Basin, through the Paris Basin, through the Low Countries to the Rhine-Ruhr. The other geostrategic region, the *Continental Eurasian,* centers around two nodes—the Soviet Industrial Triangle and North China. The two new cores of power, in Maritime Europe and in East Asia, have emerged to complement and to challenge their "senior partners."

The Maritime World includes as its geopolitical regional components: (1) Anglo-America and Caribbean, (2) Maritime Europe and the Maghreb, (3) Offshore Asia and Oceania, (4) South

America, (5) Africa South of the Sahara. The first three have a high order of internal unity, the last two have not. A unique role within the Trade-Dependent Maritime Region is played by the urbanized coastal zone, the so-called Maritime Ring, of the United States which is making the United States a truly Gulf and Pacific-facing nation to complement its Atlantic interests.

THE INTERNAL SETTING

Within the context of this pattern of geostrategic regions and their geopolitical subdivisions, neither the United States nor the Western Hemisphere is considered a region at either of the two hierarchical levels, that is, as either geopolitical or geostrategic regions, respectively. In keeping within this framework, the discussion will first focus on internal United States development and then upon the United States as part of its unique geopolitical region (Anglo-America and the Caribbean). Unity for a geopolitical region poses different problems than those for a geostrategic region. Specifically, the exercise of United States relations with Canada and the Caribbean permits less flexibility than does the exercise of these relations with other parts of the world because of the greater intimacy of the spatial ties.

Perhaps the term "the changing face of the United States" has been overworked, but it still best describes the American scene, although it often is not fully appreciated, either by outside observers or by the actors themselves. In the past three decades, a startling social and economic change has occurred over the United States landscape. The change stems from the revolutionary shift from a mixed rural-urban environment to a basically urban environment. By this it is not implied that farming has disappeared. What is emphasized is that farmers, essentially, have disappeared. As pointed out elsewhere in this volume, a small number of factory farms now shape the destinies of the rural landscape!

It is this basic fact of life, the emptying out of rural America and the concentration of the population in urban places, that supports the thesis that the United States landscape consists of two sectors: (1) the Maritime Outer Ring and (2) the Continental Inner Ring. It is the Maritime Ring, or the *Ring of the Four Seas*, that dominates the physical, cultural, and psychological life of this nation. ("Four Seas" refers to the Atlantic, Great Lakes, Gulf of Mexico, and Pacific.) Differences of place and environment account for differences in specialization within the Maritime Ring. But these differences are not great enough to overcome the community of Maritime Ring interests. The electronics worker of Mediterranean California may work in shirtsleeves and have few heating bills during the winter, in contrast to his bundled-up, snow-captured Massachusetts electronics worker counterpart. Both, however, have essentially the same economic outlook; both are vitally concerned with the national and international events affecting defense programming; both are caught up with the problems of education, race relations, and consumer spending. These are sets of interests that know few regional boundaries in the United States but are the common property of urban America.

What seems of primary regional importance from a geopolitical standpoint is not, therefore, the variety of physical, climatic, and composite geographic regions which cover the map of the United States. Rather the significance lies with the enormously space-concentrating influence of the Maritime Ring. For it is this sector (60 per cent of the United States population lives within a hundred miles of the sea) that is growing so rapidly in population and that accounts for so much of America's urbanized, manufacturing, and commercial life. If we speculate as to where a doubled United States population is likely to be located by the year 2010, it is the filling in of this Maritime Ring, both *in situ* (for there are many empty places within several miles of the biggest cities) and along now empty sectors of the Pacific, Gulf, South Atlantic, and Upper Great Lakes coasts, that is to be anticipated.

Political power, economic strength, urbanization, well-integrated land, sea and air links, foreign trade contacts—these are all characteristics of the Maritime Ring. The new frontier of the United States lies in this ring. It is in the Maritime Ring that the crucial problems of suburban dispersal, of race relations, of shorter-distance highway nets that have substantially supplanted the longer-haul transcontinental rail system, of unemployment brought on by automation, will have to be solved. It is also there that changing functions in state government, brought about by the dominance of large metropolitan centers, are being felt more keenly. (Greater Boston has 60 per cent of the population of Massachusetts; metropolitan New York has 60 per cent of the population of New York, New Jersey, and Connecticut; greater Philadelphia has 50 per cent of Pennsylvania's population; and metropolitan Los Angeles has 35 per cent of the California population.) While the need for metropolitan government is widely recognized it is generally considered from the standpoint of urban function. But the issue of preemption of state functions also cannot be avoided. Of the leading metropolitan centers, five sprawl across state lines, highlighting a need for the emergence of a new level on the political hierarchy which will be interwoven between city and state government, absorbing functions from both.

The obvious is worthy of restatement: the move to the coast and orientation to the sea has significant national psychological and strategic, as well as economic, implications. Greater American dependence on cheaply water-borne raw materials such as iron, bauxite, petroleum, wool, and hides and on finished goods such as radios, wire, automobiles, and shoes is a major element in the irrevocable involvement of the United States in a new, interdependent globalism. Of course, economic interdependence is not the sole element. The changing interest in territories off the conterminous United States continental shores has added new dimensions to America's external outlook. Today the United States is a Pacific- and a Gulf of Mexico-oriented nation, as well as an Atlantic-turning power. Consequently the need for an interdependence with the Caribbean and Offshore Asia must be viewed as part of an expanded set of geopolitical interests that complement historic ties with Canada and Maritime Europe. Cuba represents not simply a military problem as it relates to Soviet arms and economic influence immediately off the United States coast; Cuba is more than a military-ideological problem stemming from use of the island as a center for subverting Latin American governments; Cuba is a psychological problem because the fastest-growing state in the United States (Florida has had a 79 per cent increase in ten years and is the second largest absolute growth state) is only ninety miles from Cuba. The citizens of Florida feel psychologically insecure because of this proximity. Their national representatives (twelve congressmen today as compared to only eight in 1950) represent a powerful pressure group in expressing the concerns of Floridians.

To the west and north of the conterminous United States, statehood for Alaska and Hawaii has created another important spatial extension of influence with national and international ramifications for the American people. New sets of relations with such countries as Japan and Australia, indeed with Offshore Asia as a whole, are likely to represent one of the most meaningful historic trends in American foreign affairs. The problems of the United States as a Pacific Ocean basin power are no longer merely problems related to dependent territories and physically and economically remote realms. They are problems that all national states experience with their nearest neighbors, and the resolution of such problems will have to be based on recognition of this new geopolitical relationship.

THE REGIONAL SETTING

This geopolitical view of the United States and the Caribbean is an intraregional one. Canada, too, lies within this region, but for reasons of space and because of the more obvious nature of the forces—economic, military, racial, cultural, political; and spatial which lend geopolitical unity to these two countries—it will not be included in this discussion. *Place* looms large in any realistic assessment of these relations, as has previously been suggested.

For the United States, which is in the process of acquiring a Gulf and Pacific-oriented urban economy to complement that of the Atlantic-Great Lakes sector, the role of water-borne commerce via the Panama Canal is likely to become considerably more important than ever dreamed of in the past. Economically, the Panama Canal, or its successor, may have certain obvious parallels with the Suez Canal. Geopolitically, however, there is one overriding difference. The Panama Canal links two sides of a cohesive national entity—the East and West of the United States. In this sense, the parallel between Britain's relationship to Suez and that of the United States to the Panama Canal breaks down because of the change of Britain from Empire to Commonwealth status. With movement of bulk goods by sea providing a five to ten times cost superiority over rail movement, it is unreasonable to anticipate that the United States would tolerate any serious threat to its unity of movement by sea over international waters that at one and the same time serve as internal sea links.

In addition to *place*, the concept of *economic complementarity* plays an important role in the consideration of geopolitical regionalization. Complementarity of natural resources and of economies is a strong force for geopolitical unity. However, complementarity is not a simple supply-demand condition but a two-way exchange. Producers of extractive products for the advanced economies regard such exchange as exploitation, not complementarity. True complementarity occurs through specialized exchanges between equally advanced economies when both peoples derive benefits from value added by manufacturing. Japan and Australia can arrive at such complementarity, as have the United States and Maritime Europe. In the absence of technological and social equality, exploitation will mark such exchange unless the higher economic order is willing to share its profits by direct aid, investments, loans, and human efforts to redress the balance. Formerly, the powerful nations of the Northern Hemisphere assumed that differences in climate, soils, degree of industrialization could be in and of themselves converted into a basis for economic and geopolitical unity. Politicians and strategists projected such a force along a north-south axis, such as connects the United States and the Caribbean. Today, it is generally acknowledged that only genuine complementarity can be cited as a force for geopolitical unity. Genuine complementarity means a two-way, not a one-way street, with each side obtaining its fair share of value added by manufacturing. Such complementarity will exist when Venezuelan crude oil and iron ore, Jamaican bauxite and alumina, Honduran timber and bananas, Cuban sugar and Guatemalan coffee are exchanged along with Latin American steel wire, fine furniture, veneer panels, chocolate, frozen fish, banana cake, fishing nets, and shoes—in return for United States raw materials as well as finished products.

One can, of course, become overly sanguine about the prospects for overnight change. The changed Puerto Rican economy (cement, textiles, shoes, plastics, electronics, tourism) is the result of a special set of relations with the United States. How well would "Operation Bootstrap" have succeeded without the immigration valve of New York City, let alone tax subsidies and a favorable and protected climate for United States investment?

While much remains to be done by the United States to stimulate genuine complementarity, action also has to be taken by Caribbean countries among themselves. To talk of a Caribbean common market is no longer pure fancy. With outside assistance, regional planning, and harmonious resource allocation much can be done through internal efforts. It is not necessary to speak of sophisticated items of exchange in this context, but rather of such mundane articles as processed food, clothing, furniture, building material, soaps, shoes. These can be exchanged within Caribbean America, given the proper political, economic, and psychological milieu. As a specific example, the trade potential of the Venezuelan furniture industry with nearby offshore islands can be cited. What is required, above all, is an imaginative planning and distributional approach.

THE INTERNATIONAL SETTING

As with any other major nation, the posture of the United States in international affairs cannot be examined through a series of discrete, isolated actions in diverse parts of the world. This posture has global earth-space parameters, and, indeed, outer space ones as well.

Geographical analysis usually begins and ends with place. But place only becomes geographical when recognized as a particular part of the earth's surface within which certain processes interact spatially to create unique area associations. To evaluate these area associations, insight into the dimensions of scale, time, and movement is necessary. Thus what is measured and analyzed in considering the United States within a national scale as the amalgam of diverse internal regions, is quite different from analysis of the country at the international scale. Since process change occurs over time, all geographical problems have a temporal aspect. To think of America's changing position in world affairs from the context of the self-sufficient America of pre-World War II to the globally interdependent one of today; or of the shift of

Negro America from its exclusively rural southern locale of the 1920's and 1930's to the great urban centers of the north is to utilize the time scale as an aid in evaluating spatial trends.

Movement, the third dimension, is the vehicle through which the dynamism of earth-man relations is established. Movement involves men, goods, and ideas, and includes such diverse processes as immigration, trade, exchange of ideas, weathering, shrinking of water bodies, or port and railway construction. Jet-age movement, including long-distance travel with the assistance of mid-air refueling, or the use of communications satellites for news and other television purposes, is a dimension of major proportions in understanding America's ability to reach outward today.

There is no single view of the global setting that would be accepted without qualification by all nations as a view of reality. For each nation is egocentric, and reality is *its* reality. Geographers have held views of the earth since the times of Hecateus and Strabo and will continue to expound them, subject to the influence of scale, time, movement, and, of course, personal background and outlook. Thus, when an American geographer looks at the world at large, he looks at it from a particular and undeniably nationally oriented vantage point. This does not, however, imply an inevitably narrow, partisan base, for recognition of one's own perceptional background can help the observer to maintain balance and objectivity.

To speak of the United States as part of a distinct geostrategic world is to recognize a state of global interdependence. Such a state is part of a continuing process which has led America from its periods of isolationism, continental expansion, and global egocentrism to the present era of global interdependence. With the help of vast space, abundance of natural resources, a unique economic system, and open immigration, the United States achieved self-sufficiency and an economy of abundance. But no means has been found to restrain this abundance. Because of the competitive nature of the domestic economy, the chemical-technological-automation revolution, the commitments that arose from involvement in two world wars, and the perceived need to help rehabilitate or develop other nations, the United States has found itself plunged into an era of superabundance—an era which builds on and yet partly weakens the base of self-sufficiency, in return for a broader base which includes international exchange to maintain economic and political momentum.

Whether other nations, such as the Soviet Union, once having achieved the goal of abundance through self-sufficiency, can and will move into this subsequent phase, remains to be seen. But certainly America's superabundance is inextricably intertwined with her global strategic posture.

It has been previously suggested that the Anglo-American and Caribbean geopolitical region is part of the Trade-Dependent Maritime World. The step up in the regional hierarchy from the geopolitical to the geostrategic represents an enormous leap in scale and range of complexity. It is within the context of this complexity that United States relations with South America, Maritime Europe, Offshore Asia, and Africa can be most clearly appreciated. For the United States today, various alliance problems that may arise within the Organization of American States, the North Atlantic Treaty Organization, or the Anzus Pact cannot be regarded as independent and isolated. Certainly, when it comes to the weighing of American capabilities and needs, the issue is not a North Atlantic Alliance versus an Alliance for Progress, nor is it a Maritime Pacific Concord versus a Maritime Atlantic Concord. The issue is not *either, or;* it is *both.* Japan, Brazil, Spain and Argentina, Canada and Jamaica—and yes, the United States and Cuba. These are parts of one Trade-Dependent Maritime World. The concept of a Trade-Dependent Maritime World including, as it does, not only Anglo-America and the Caribbean, but also Maritime Europe and the Maghreb, Offshore Asia, South America, and Africa South of the Sahara, represents a level of spatial generalization that must allow for nonconformi-

ties and for differences in degree of association. Given such qualification, the qualities of this global-embracing maritime realm
can be briefly assessed. First, and most importantly, this realm
does not include the entire Eurasian littoral—that is, those lands
of the Middle East, South Asia, Southeast Asia, and East Asia
which were included in Halford Mackinder's classical Inner or
Marginal Crescent and Nicholas Spykman's Eurasian Rimland.
Only Maritime Europe, of all Eurasia's littoral, is classed as part
of the Maritime Geostrategic region.

Unlike previous political geographic interpretations, this view
of the global setting excludes most of the Eurasian littoral, either
because qualities of a genuine maritime-oriented area are absent
(both South and East Asia are continental-type land masses, with
broad, nonspecialized agricultural bases), or because contiguity to
substantial Eurasian continental power has checkmated the exercise of dominant strategic control by the Maritime World (the
shatterbelt regions of the Middle East and Southeast Asia, where
outside maritime power had been the dominant force in the European Colonial Era).

The region designated as the Trade-Dependent Maritime
World does not consist of every piece of land that adjoins the
open seas, because maritime orientation is not satisfied by coastal
locale alone. There must also be included useful ports and harbors; access to the hinterland and to mass populations; seamind-
edness; and an economic structure that depends on international
trade, either because of advantages of product specialization or
because of the absence of a broad base for relative self-sufficiency.
Thus, the maritime geostrategic region is global-embracing, but
does not include *all* ocean-fronting regions.

A major unifying feature of this realm is contiguity by sea to
either or both of the dominant power cores (the Maritime Ring
of the United States and urbanized Maritime Europe). Other features include: coastal orientation of rapidly urbanizing populations; national states that have either limited land areas or lim-

ited populations, a phenomenon that intensifies the need for national economic specialization; and overseas trade. Brazil, the exception to limitation of land or population, possesses the other two features. Even Africa South of the Sahara, so much of which is landlocked, is far more oriented to the sea than it is internally, considering the weight of populations and economies of such nations as Nigeria, Ghana, the Republic of South Africa, and Tanzania.

The major asset that the United States and its European allies possess in their relations with the rest of this Maritime World is better access via sea-air lanes, as compared to the access possessed by the Eurasian Continental realm. This has proved no slight advantage in the cold-hot war struggles that have ranged from Cuba, Guatemala, and British Guiana, to the Congo, Tanzania, African members of the French Community, to the Philippines, and Taiwan. The commercial food and fibers and mineral fuels of coastal and associated interior lowlands, and the metallic minerals of coastal-adjoining highlands are readily available for exchange by sea. Moreover, the ameliorating climatic effects of open seas upon coastlands have assisted temporary and permanent Western settlement or economic development ventures. The significance of the maritime qualities of this realm to American military and political strategy can scarcely be overemphasized.

Emergence of Maritime Europe as a second power node within the Trade-Dependent Maritime World has been rapid and not without accompanying tensions. But such tensions between the United States and Maritime Europe as over Suez, NATO, the Common Market, Southeast Asia, and Mainland China should be regarded as evolutionary stages in Maritime Europe's development as a genuinely equal power core. Despite some very genuine differences, interdependence and mutual vulnerability of this set of cores continue to serve as centripetal geostrategic forces. The existence of multiple cores within a geostrategic region is likely, in the long run, to serve as a major unifier with regard to the region's peripheral areas. For none of the less developed parts of a geostrategic region desires to be totally dependent upon one core. South America's interests in striking a more balanced stage of interaction with Maritime Europe, as well as African ties with the United States, are examples, the former calculated to lessen South America's fear of United States dominance, the latter to lessen African fear of European dominance.

A brief explanation of the Offshore Asian concept is warranted, the other units within the Maritime Geostrategic region being somewhat more self-explanatory. The countries included are Japan, South Korea, Taiwan, the Philippines, Australia, and New Zealand. While Offshore Asia may appear to exhibit considerable uniqueness as a geopolitical region, its morphologic character and functional organization have much in common with other maritime geopolitical regions. *Place* includes a sea orientation and a sea-mindedness that can be likened to that of Maritime Europe (granted the more recent entry of Offshore Asia into the lists of modern industrial nations). *Overseas trade* is a prerequisite for all the states of Offshore Asia, either because their economies have specialized to compensate for lack of a broad domestic resource base, or, in the case of Australia, because youth, limited population, and Empire-Commonwealth ties have encouraged such specialization. *Relative political stability* and *national cultural unity,* certainly related to insular positions, are other characteristics.

Japan's role as the core of the region is still in an emergent form. Immaturity of intraregional trade ties and the political-military restraints upon Japan's activities that stem from World War II are responsible for this. But, by weight of population (60 per cent of the region's total), economic strength, and strategic-economic ties to the United States, Japan's position of leadership in Offshore Asia is being consolidated. It is also to be noted that Offshore Asia is too limited a region to satisfy Japan's needs for international trade—a characteristic held in common with Maritime Europe's industrial core area.

For Offshore Asia, Australia offers the major areas of effective national territory and empty area. Such areas are likely to be used as bases for economic development and intraregional economic complementarity. In one aspect of movement, immigration, there is a marked contrast between Offshore Asia and Maritime Europe. Within the latter, population mobility enhances social complementarity; within the former, absence of mobility is the characteristic feature. Australia's subtle "White Only" immigration policy is not likely to be altered substantially, a policy tending to neutralize some of the unifying effects of regional economic and strategic complementarity. One might venture the hope that some compromise will be found between total exclusion and unlimited immigration, as evidenced by recent modifications of the law to permit families to join Asian migrants more easily.

The rationale for the Maritime European-Maghreb unit also merits brief explanation. To consider Maritime Europe and the Maghreb as one geopolitical region is to recognize the breadth and depth of trans-Mediterranean ties, rather than to be diverted by the veneer of current political tides. Ease of communications, complementarity of peoples and products, strategic interdependence, and historic association are basic magnets of geopolitical attraction. The presence of over half a million Algerians in France, the role of French language, culture, and economic aid in North Africa, the linking impact of Saharan petroleum and natural gas, and Maritime Europe's real and imagined needs to secure its southern approaches are major long-range ties. These help to explain the ironically intimate, if at the same time still tentative, Franco-Algerian alliance. They also help to explain the limits beyond which other North African Arab states such as Tunisia and Morocco appear unwilling to proceed in making common cause with their Middle Eastern Arab neighbors against Maritime Europe in such issues as the Arab-Israeli conflict.

Turning to the Eurasian Continental World, with its two geopolitical regions, (1) Soviet Heartland and Eastern Europe, and (2) East Asia, geographers recognize that the recent emergence of the Soviet Union as a strong, unified national state with strategic control of Eastern Europe to the Elbe River represents the unity of the Heartland that Halford Mackinder foresaw. Indeed this is even a broader unity, because Mackinder's Heartland extended from the Elbe to the Yenisei, but did not include eastern Siberia. Such a unity has not, however, brought to the Heartland command over Maritime Europe, or over most other parts of the Eurasian Rimland. Even with respect to East Asia, Heartland unity has not resulted in automatic dominance of the former by the latter. Instead, the Heartland shares a complex set of relationships with allies, neutrals, and enemies and, in the case of China, with a sharply competitive "quasi-ally."

The increased tempo and scale of Soviet international involvement has a tendency to divert attention from the internal scene. In fact, however, within its borders the U.S.S.R. is as deeply involved as ever in its historic task of developing the resource base in the face of such barriers as distance, emptiness, and diversely rigorous landscape, and this very internal involvement is one of the dynamics of Soviet foreign policy. While shifts of population and recasted strategies of economic organization are major characteristics of this development process, reliance upon long-distance hauling remains a constant and fixed factor, with long-term implications for trade, aid, and other foreign ties.

The most important spatial aspect of this internal development is landward orientation or continentality. Unlike United States expansion westward, which has had as its goal the favorably endowed maritime reaches of the Great Lakes, the Gulf of Mexico, and the Pacific, Soviet eastward expansion is, essentially, directed to landward areas. In contemporary terms, the meaning of such an orientation is twofold: trade contacts with the outside world are becoming increasingly penalized by distance, because greater dependence on landward forms of bulk transportation, more costly and less flexible than sea carriers, adversely affects total transportation costs; and contact with bordering Asian countries has become more intimate, with greater exercise of Soviet strategic power on its borderlands.

One might ask whether the United States, with an economy that has developed in stimulated response to regional specialization, does not show parallels with the Soviet experience. The differences, however, are more significant than the parallels. Development of the Gulf and West Coast regions of the United States has taken place within far more favorable physical settings and with better water- and land-borne access to the major population and economic core of the Northeast. Moreover, national self-sufficiency has not served as the tail to wag the dog: witness the use and dependence on such foreign materials as iron ore, copper, petroleum, sugar cane, meat, and both raw and finished steels. The United States has passed from the age of national self-sufficiency to the era of superabundance and global interdependence, for self-sufficiency cannot satisfy an economy of superabundance which must seek out foreign markets.

This American geographer, in viewing the Soviet setting, concludes that the strategic character and needs of the U.S.S.R. are different from those of the United States, these differences arising from the combination of place, scale, time, and movement. The farther eastward the extension of Soviet development areas, the greater the liability of reaching outward, certainly beyond Eurasia. Communist party policies of achieving self-sufficiency have remained a consistent national aim and are reinforced by the need to open up remote interior areas populated by national minorities, to provide the latter with the means for economic development.

From a strategic point of view, development of the interior coupled with the common boundary that the U.S.S.R. has with fourteen countries in Eurasia, and with the fact that many minority peoples lie astride these boundaries, strengthens the Soviet land position in Eurasia. It is increasingly difficult for the Maritime World to compete with the U.S.S.R. along that inward-

facing portion of the Eurasian land mass (from Afghanistan eastward) that is more clearly connected to the continental interior
than to the sea. Chinese protestations to the contrary, the
U.S.S.R. is both a European and an Asian power.

Once, however, one looks beyond the land boundary confines
of the Soviet Union, the strategic liabilities of its position continue to persist. Soviet political and military globalism has pulled
the U.S.S.R. into strategic area ventures, where its capacities do
not match its appetite.[1] The Caribbean and Africa are perhaps the
clearest examples, but Southeast Asia, unless tackled jointly with
China, is likely to stand as another. Recognition of this liability
doubtless was the basis for the post-World War II port and
naval base ventures in Tirana, Alexandria, Latakia, and Hodeida
—not all of which have proven unqualified successes. But continued involvement in such Middle East ventures as Yemen, for
example, suggests that the eastern Mediterranean has become the
major "offensive zone" for the U.S.S.R., at least in terms of guarantee of access if not outright control. Past emphasis on the Black
Sea and the Straits, as well as the Baltic, was essentially defensive,
for Soviet fear of attack through the water routes was well
founded. Today's emphasis, however, is far more offensive, in the
total political-economic-military sense. Never before has Russia
had so large a potential stake in the Straits-Suez Canal-Indian
Ocean-Far East sea route, as reflected by its merchant vessel and
submarine programs.

The foregoing might tempt one to draw a tight analogy between the role of the Panama Canal vis-à-vis the United States, in
the eastern Mediterranean-Indian Ocean vis-à-vis the U.S.S.R.
However, the objective situation remains substantially different,
because of the heavier volume of trade and the relative significance of America's Pacific coastlands to the core area; and the

[1] In the June 1967 Arab-Israeli war, this strategic limitation of the Soviet
position in the eastern Mediterranean was underscored. Despite its commitments to the Arabs, the U.S.S.R. could not intervene directly because of
United States strategic control of the air and water.

absence of strong intervening powers in the Caribbean in contrast to the eastern Mediterranean-Indian Ocean situation, where both Western and indigenous power stakes are high.

Turning to the setting for Sino-Soviet relations, the view is repeated that East Asia lies within a geostrategic region that has two parts: (1) the Soviet Union and Eastern Europe and (2) East Asia. Cultural, racial, and physical environmental conditions distinguish the two parts, and the internal ideological rift within the Communist camp has heightened this distinction.

On the other hand, the drive against "The Enemy Without" is more than simply a common drive against the external non-Communist world. The fact is that two developing countries such as China and the U.S.S.R., with so extensive a land border and such potential for complementarity, cannot ignore one another. One might, of course, postulate that just as Western Europe and Eastern Europe have built an "Iron Curtain" to separate one from the other, so could this conceivably be the case for Sino-Soviet relations. But here the parallel ends. Western Europe is a maritime region with specialized economic links and close physical ties to its trans-atlantic partner. China is not a maritime-oriented region. It is a land power. Its back is to the sea and its potential for self-sufficiency is considerable, albeit a lesser one than that of the Soviet Union. China's relations with its trans-Pacific neighbors have, even with ideological harmony, lacked the order of economic, cultural, and strategic involvement that marks United States-Maritime European relations.

Just as the two North Atlantic regions have become increasingly interdependent strategically and economically, so have the two Eurasian continental geopolitical units. Traditionally, the U.S.S.R. has feared the pressures on its Siberian lands that might be exerted from Chinese Turkestan, Outer Mongolia, and Manchuria. In recent decades these pressures originated from Japan or even from the more distant Pacific-held bases of the Western world. In the future, whatever pressures are exerted will emanate from Mainland Chinese areas that are within the strategic reach of Soviet land power.

As Soviet agriculture and industry continue to spread into Russian central Asia, central Siberia, and the Far Eastern provinces, the U.S.S.R. will surely become more vulnerable to Chinese pressures. At the same time, the greater Soviet stake in Asia and increased Siberian self-sufficiency are likely both to force and enable the U.S.S.R. to find a modus vivendi with its neighbor. Extension of the Chinese frontier northeastward (Manchuria) and northwestward (Chinese Mongolia and Sinkiang) is likely to have the same effect on Chinese relations with the Soviet Union.

Surely there are scales of strategic involvement which complicate any neat pattern of major power relationships that one might venture to draw. Communist China's stake and sense of involvement in Southeast Asia, where she holds a primacy of interest, will not always coincide with Soviet interests, particularly in terms of emphasis and timing. The same can be said for Sino-Indian relations, which, from China's standpoint, involve the integrity of her territorial connections (Sinkiang-Tibet). The Soviet Union, on the other hand, has a set of interests in South Asia, especially in India, which operate at a different scale from those of China. Not tactical border problems, but broader ideological considerations related to Soviet ambitions in South and East Asia, and, indeed, in Africa, put matters here in different perspective for the U.S.S.R. The difference is therefore one of geostrategic versus geopolitical perspective. Of course, the complications of land border length, of population pressures, and of ethnic minorities mean far greater complexity and energy expenditures in reconciliation of Sino-Soviet differences, as compared with United States-Maritime European internal conflicts.

Considered in another way, the sensitivity of the Soviet Union to strategic problems with its nearest neighbors, which include not only Maritime Europe but also the United States, is quite different from the sensitivity of China to the United States, which is perceived not as a nearest neighbor, but as a distant intervener, whose East Asia interests are operated for foreign and tenuous bases.

Granted these differences, the overriding forces that contribute to a unity of strategic purposes are, we believe, of sufficient magnitude to accept the Sino-Soviet world as a strategic unity and to plan both strategy and tactics in accordance with this thesis.

Where the two great strategic worlds meet most directly, in the Middle East and Southeast Asia, we can continue to expect the kinds of confrontation that have taken place since World War II. In each of these shatterbelts, great power relations are complicated by the fact that only one, and the lesser of each set of power cores, directly confronts the greater adversary. In the Middle East during 1956, where Maritime Europe was in direct confrontation with the U.S.S.R., it was the United States which made common cause with the Soviet Union to limit and eventually extinguish the Franco-British attempt to maintain its Middle Eastern position. Is this not analogous to today's situation, where, in Southeast Asia, China finds itself in direct confrontation with American power, and the Soviet Union seems to have common interest with the United States in preventing escalation?

We are not overly sanguine about the prospects of either of these regions becoming neutralized in the foreseeable future, nor do we feel that either the Maritime World or the continental Eurasian powers have any decided advantages in the struggle over the shatterbelts. We do feel that there are areas which are more favorable to one of the protagonists rather than the other, and place Malaysia and Thailand as particularly favorable areas from which the Maritime World can contest Sino-Soviet pressures in Southeast Asia, in contrast to Vietnam and Laos, wherein tactical, historical, and ideological conditions militate against American efforts. Turkey and Israel afford the Maritime World possibilities of stable partnership bases in the Middle East.

DYNAMIC GEOPOLITICAL EQUILIBRIUM

Geopolitical equilibrium is a dynamic, not a static state. Equilibrium is maintained by fluid lines of influence radiating outward from power nodes, reflecting changed conditions within those nodes as well as within peripheral areas of power application. Forces contributing to this dynamism include: (1) population explosion, (2) rising economic needs, (3) increasing ubiquitousness of raw materials and greater ease of transfer and use, (4) emergence of new, closed national political space in some parts of the world simultaneous with breakdown of national barriers in other parts, and (5) spread of nuclear weapons capabilities. Desires to achieve genuine economic complementarity, national drives for political and psychological equality, and alternative means of improved movement, modify more commonly used elements of geopolitical analysis, such as: distributional patterns and space relations of people and materials framed within unique physical, ideological, and historical settings and oriented to one dominating arena of movement.

To maintain dynamic equilibrium, horizontal and vertical adjustments, analogous to the combination of horizontal and vertical crustal movements that occur in isostatic processes, take place on the geopolitical scene. In these vertical adjustments, not only technological change in resource use, but group will, efforts, and myths play crucial roles. Thus, geopolitical equilibrium was dynamically maintained when the Middle East was lost to the West and instead became a shatterbelt, partly because this loss occurred at a time when Maritime European economic and military strength rose in compensation through internal developments and partly through the discovery and exploitation of North African petroleum.

In other instances, horizontal alignment changes take place to maintain geopolitical equilibrium without involving compensating vertical changes. Loss of Cuba to the Western fold found its compensation level in the strengthened ties between the United States and such (Organization of American States) partners as Venezuela, Brazil, and Chile, not in any significant internal changes within the United States.

Similar examples can be drawn from the Communist world. From the international power sense, weakening of Soviet Union ties with China has been compensated by the success of the U.S.S.R. space effort. Horizontal shifts in alignment between the U.S.S.R. and Albania found their compensation in a renewal of more positive Soviet-Yugoslav relations.

The foregoing view of America in its geopolitical setting rests upon the assumption that spatial variability in international geopolitical processes can provide a framework for a viable geopolitical system today. Geopolitical equilibrium does not exist as a consequence of any "natural" order. Instead, it comes into being when men through their political institutions perceive and welcome its rationale for existence. Because of this, geographers of all nations have a continuing responsibility for inquiring into the nature of such systems.

SUGGESTED READINGS

Cohen, S. B., *Geography and Politics in a World Divided*. New York: Random House, 1963; London: Methuen, 1964.

Cohen, S. B., "Geopolitical Equilibrium and the Sino-Soviet World," in A. Gyorgy (ed.), *Issues of World Communism*. Princeton, N.J.: Van Nostrand, 1966, pp. 151–171.

Deutsch, K., *Nationalism and Social Communication*. Cambridge, Mass.: Technology Press of M.I.T., 1953.

Ginsburg, N. S., *Atlas of Economic Development*. Chicago: University of Chicago Press, 1961.

Mackinder, H., *Democratic Ideals and Reality* (*1919*). New York: Norton, 1962.

Sprout, H. M., *The Ecological Perspective on Human Affairs*. Princeton, N. J.: Princeton University Press, 1965.

Spykman, N., *The Geography of the Peace*. New York: Harcourt, Brace, 1942.

12 ON GEOGRAPHY AND ECONOMIC DEVELOPMENT

Norton S. Ginsburg

No two countries are alike. Some are large; some small; some old; some new. Some are rich, and some are poor. Geographers, like other social scientists, are interested in why some countries are apparently wealthier than others, or, to put it another way, more highly developed economically. They are, therefore, interested in the kinds of resources with which countries are endowed, and they are interested in the ways in which these resources are employed to attain given ends. Perhaps more important, they are interested in the distribution of wealth and poverty, and in the regional patterns of livelihood and levels of living that tend to be obscured until revealed on the map.

Let us assume that we were attempting to map the geographical distribution of poverty—or, for that matter, wealth. What would such a map look like? To some extent the picture that would emerge depends upon the scale of the map. If it were of relatively large scale, say, that of a *city,* one would find pockets of poverty, of people with low incomes: in slum areas near the central business districts; on the edges of the older manufactural areas within the city; and, if one were to look at cities in Asia, Africa, or Latin America, for example, in shabby suburbs or dreary shantytowns which often string out into the countryside and ultimately form part of it.

At the scale of a *country,* one can map poverty in areas that are relatively inaccessible, ill endowed with natural resources, or "overdeveloped" in the sense that there are too many people doing too little on too little land without alternative sources of livelihood than the hard-worked soil. Even in the United States, wealthy though it is, large areas that are poor—or, shall we say, underdeveloped—can be identified. Much of the Appalachian Highlands of the eastern third of the country fall into that category, as do parts of the American Indian-inhabited Southwest, and depressed mining areas where the richer deposits have been exhausted long since or where changing technology has reduced the demand and therefore the price for the resource.

On the *world* scale, a map of underdevelopment also can be compiled, but the unit of compilation becomes the nation-state. The evolution of a closed world system tied by the linkage web of modern transportation and the creation of literally scores of new countries, especially since the close of World War II, have led to a re-examination and rephrasing of the New Testament axiom from "The Poor ye always shall have with you," to: "Need the *Poor* always be with *us?*" Even more striking, the world's deprived have begun to ask with ever louder voices: "Need the poor always be *us?*"

In nation-state terms, who are the world's poor, and where are they? What and where, in short, is the "underdeveloped world"?

Before attempting to answer these questions, it is necessary to have some understanding of what "underdevelopment" means. In one sense, it can mean any country, even the United States and the countries of Western Europe, since none of these has so completely developed its resources that poverty has been eliminated within its boundaries. In another, it could refer to countries which simply cannot exist for long, so marginal and precarious is the existence of their inhabitants; but, in fact, we know for certain of no such case. The whole concept is a comparative one. Some countries have many more goods and services available to their people than others. It is customary to describe the summation of all such goods and services within a country as its Gross National Product—or GNP. That share of GNP available to each person in a given country is its Gross National Product per Capita. When one speaks of the wealth or poverty of nations, one ordinarily has in mind Gross National Product per Capita, and it is this datum, when available, that can be mapped relatively easily.

A map based upon this measure shows a striking contrast between countries and, indeed, lends credence to the existence of not one but two worlds—one wealthier or developed, and a second poorer or lesser developed (Figure 12–1).

The developed world for the most part consists of what often is called Anglo-America, though in fact French Canada also is included; Western Europe; and Australasia. Parts of Eastern Europe and the U.S.S.R. are arrayed close behind. Of the thirty countries with the highest per capita GNP's, only seven are found outside of these regions: Argentina, Uruguay, and Venezuela in Latin America; the Union of South Africa, Japan, Kuwait, and Israel. Kuwait and Israel are special cases; both are small, Kuwait deriving its income almost solely from petroleum and with a very small population; Israel, a European cultural oasis on Near Eastern soil and still partly dependent upon outside sources of income.

The world of poverty extends over most of Latin America and Africa and encompasses almost all of Asia other than Japan. It includes over three quarters of the world's peoples, most of whom have dark skin. In fact, it appears that whereas most of the "haves" in the modern world are white, most of the "have-nots" are colored. Equally significant is the fact that most of the "have-nots" rely on agriculture for their livelihoods, whereas most of the "haves" do not.

The poorer countries lie, for the most part, in the world's lower latitudes, within the parallel 30° North and South; only about one fifth lie beyond these bounds. The fact suggests that the

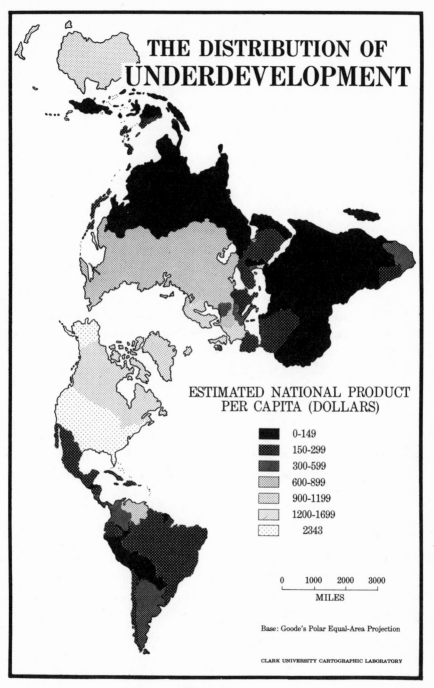

THE DISTRIBUTION OF
UNDERDEVELOPMENT

ESTIMATED NATIONAL PRODUCT
PER CAPITA (DOLLARS)

■	0-149
■	150-299
■	300-599
▨	600-899
▨	900-1199
▨	1200-1699
▨	2343

0   1000   2000   3000

MILES

Base: Goode's Polar Equal-Area Projection

CLARK UNIVERSITY CARTOGRAPHIC LABORATORY

Figure 12–1

lower latitudes and particularly the equatorial ones present special limitations upon the abilities of men to use the resources with which nature has endowed the territories in which they live.

Superficially, it seems to be a reasonable hypothesis that these regions are naturally inferior to those of middle latitudes; certainly there is some justification for this proposition. Tropical soils are notoriously poor and infertile. Although they often carry a cover of lush forest vegetation, forest and soils coexist in a state of precarious equilibrium in which the soil is enriched by the rapid decay of vegetable matter but only so long as it is not exposed to intense leaching by tropical downpours or to the desiccating and destructive effects of the high low-latitude sun. Once the vegetation cover is cleared, such soils decrease so rapidly in fertility that most of them are employed only in a system of shifting cultivation, a kind of crop rotation, whereby land rather than crops is changed from year to year.

Many such regions also are characterized by a superabundance of precipitation, and insects and other pests abound. Only certain crops can tolerate this first condition. Rice is one, but being a photoperiodic plant it does less well in regions near the equator where the days are short and cloudiness high than it does where the days are longer and spells of dryness occur during the growing season. Thus, even rice yields, like those of most other such crops, are very low in equatorial regions. Certain tree crops, especially those which come nearest to re-creating the original forest environment, such as rubber, do much better under tropical conditions.

On the other hand, the lower latitudes have at least one enormous advantage for agriculture, their length of growing season. Most low-latitude regions have year-round growing seasons which permit the multiple cropping of a given piece of land. On the outskirts of Singapore, for example, six or seven crops of vegetables are grown by Chinese horticulturists in a given year, admittedly by special measures such as careful hand watering and the application of truly remarkable quantities of both organic and inorganic fertilizers and under special circumstances exemplified by the large, nearby Singapore vegetable market.

Given the enormous advantage of year-round solar energy surely, one might argue, modern technology can solve the problems of low soil fertility and low productivity. What about chemical fertilizers and plant strains resistant to insects and blight? Unfortunately, most advances in soil technology have focused on middle-latitude, not tropical residual, soils, which have peculiar characteristics of their own and which are often singularly unresponsive to types of fertilizers used successfully elsewhere. For lack of incentives to do otherwise, modern agricultural technology at least has, with few exceptions, neglected the problems of the lower latitudes. Of all the major world grains, rice, the most important to more people than any other, is the least understood and the least affected by the technological revolution in agriculture, especially insofar as it may be raised within the tropics and despite greatly improved yields in Spain, Japan, and the United States.

Of course, many aspects of modern technology *do* apply to the tropical regions as well as to others. Swamps can be drained, hillsides terraced, streams dammed and bridged, insectides applied, environmental sanitation pressed forward. But all of these measures require sizable amounts of capital, as indeed does research and development of the sort needed to utilize more effectively tropical soils and raise crop yields; and in most of the tropical world such capital has been in short supply. It has been in short supply less because that world is inherently poor than because most of it has been dominated, until recently, for a century or more by middle-latitude European powers. The latter were unwilling to commit their own resources to solution of these problems; they were more interested in that kind of resource exploitation—mineral, forest, and specialized commercial crops—which gave greater returns more rapidly and at much less cost. Thus, the new countries of the tropics have come into being in a world less well equipped to deal with many of *their* resource problems than any other, and at the same time short of capital with which to attempt solutions themselves.

It is also argued that the low latitudes are too hot, rainy, and humid to be comfortable, and that human energy is drained away before it can be applied productively to the resource endowment. Two rebuttals, one historical, one contemporary, pertain here. There is much historical evidence that great civilizations have evolved in the tropics—in Dravidian South India, in Ceylon, in Java, in Cambodia, in Nigeria—although admittedly none of these have survived to this day. On the other hand, neither has Rome. Second, the more rapidly applicable aspects of modern technology can greatly alleviate the discomforts and disadvantages of the tropical regions. Plenty of pure piped water, fans and air conditioning, insecticides, and machines to save human energy all can contribute notably, though at high cost, to man's ability to produce and to live in comparative comfort.

The case of Malaya is worth citing here. Under a relatively enlightened colonial administration, the Malayan economy developed rapidly before World War II, though not equally so in all sectors. Roads, railways, municipal water supplies, environmental sanitation, new types and varieties of tree crops supported by continuing research and development, electricity and all of its concomitants, have helped make the country eminently livable, if deplorably hot at midday, and provided the area, even after independence, with the second highest level of living in Asia, and higher than that in Spain. Certainly, the resource endowments of somewhat similar low-latitude countries ought to be able to provide as satisfactory a basis for development, all other things being equal—which, of course, they never are.

A few of the lower-latitude poorer countries and several of these at higher latitudes are associated with climates characterized by perennial or seasonal aridity. Among these are particularly the countries of the Near East, including those of North Africa. Traditionally, these areas have been associated with a combination of oasis cultivation and pastoral nomadism. The lower Nile and Tigris-Euphrates valleys can be likened to gigantic oases, and they are densely populated.

Unlike the moist, low-latitude regions, the opportunities for expanding agricultural land in these areas are distinctly limited, although expansion through great irrigation projects is technologically possible in some cases, as in Israel's Negev, but only at great cost. Raising productivity in the already occupied oasis-type areas is technologically more promising, though still costly, as witness the constuction of the second Aswan Dam in Egypt. The problem is vastly complicated, however, by the intensity of occupance associated with traditional systems of cultivation and a concomitant marginality of agriculture, which makes the raising of capital from agricultural surpluses unlikely and implementation of measures of rationalization—of land ownership, of technological improvements, of large-scale water control—extremely difficult. The situation in the Near East is ameliorated somewhat, in the cases of countries like Saudi Arabia, Libya, and Iraq, where petroleum is produced in large quantities and brings in substantial foreign exchange, but the economic system in each of these cases makes it difficult to innovate either in agriculture or in industrial development. Here, low literacy rates are as much a factor in retarding economic growth as are limited resource endowments, whether for agriculture or for industry.

In addition to countries that have problems of agricultural development in part because of aridity or of excessive heat and moisture, there are others, not necessarily in the lower latitudes, whose poverty is associated with what has been called "overdevelopment." This word refers to a situation in which occupance of a given region has been so long and successful in pre-modern terms that huge populations have grown to the limits of subsistence under a given technology, but only at low levels of living and economic productivity. Such areas resemble the intensive traditional type of development that one finds in the oases in the arid regions referred to above. To a degree the case is illustrated by the Indo-Gangetic plain in the north of India or the Tonkin delta of North Vietnam.

But the most striking and significant examples are found in China, at least until recently and probably still. About half the population of China, that is, over 300 million people, live in the lower valley of the Yangtze River and in the North China plain, Asia's largest middle-latitude alluvial plain. Although both drought and flood are major ingredients in the ecological patterns found in these areas, the basic problem is one of too many people on too little land, even though that land is relatively fertile and modern technology can be rather readily adapted to it. The Chinese long ago developed an agricultural system which produced astonishingly high yields per unit area—through the intensive use of night soil as fertilizer, the partial control of water for irrigation and flood control, concentration on crops designed to give high yields under the environmental circumstances extant, multiple cropping, and above all through extraordinary quantities of labor inputs. Unfortunately, not only are greater labor inputs not possible, but even if they were they would not be likely to produce higher yields than those already attained. Even now, rural underemployment, at least seasonally, is rife; and the system as a whole has become fossilized.

What, then, can be done? Certainly some improvements in yields can be obtained through the use of modern technology, especially with regard to the improvement of crop strains, shifts to chemical fertilizers, and the more rational use of labor by merging an infinity of minute plots of land, individually owned and worked, into much larger production units. Herein lies one of the major justifications for the creation of the communes in China under the Communist regime. In addition, mechanization can be applied to certain kinds of facilities, as indeed it already has in Japan—to more efficient pumps for irrigation, to the threshing and milling of already harvested grain and to some extent to harvesting itself, and to the transportation of produce from country to city and from regions of surplus to regions of deficit.

On the other hand, increases in productivity from these sources are likely to be modest, and they are likely to be least from mechanization, even where possible, than from the application of scientific knowledge to cultivation, since mechanization in agriculture tends to be more labor-saving than productive of higher unit-area yields.

More important, even the relative efficiencies of the commune in China cannot reduce the rural population unless other, non-agricultural employment opportunities are found for a large percentage of the growing rural population. To provide an economic infrastructure that will permit such labor diversion, the Chinese have been investing heavily in industrial development, not only in existing cities, but also in other areas especially favored by the availability of natural resources such as coal. Such industrial development not only is expensive, and China like most poorer countries is capital short, it also is slow relative to the enormity of the basic problem, which continues to grow.

The possibilities of solving this problem may be seen in the case of Japan, the agricultural population of which has remained nearly constant for most of a century, while the total population has trebled. The growth increments of Japan's population have been siphoned off into the industrializing cities, and the economy as a whole has shifted strikingly within the last thirty years to one that is based more on industrial and commercial activities than upon agriculture. Although the example of Japan is readily observable by all developing countries, it is of lesser value than one might suppose for at least two reasons.

First, even to the Japanese it is far from clear just how the interlocking processes of industrialization, modern urbanization, and social readjustment have taken place, although more is known about them now than as recently as the close of World War II. Second, the Japanese launched their economic development under particularly advantageous circumstances; they were, in short, ahead of the game. The presently poor countries seeking development are, by way of contrast, in a sense competitive with one another, and they operate in a world that is close enough to restrict adventurism and, certainly, traditional imperialism. Equally important, the Japanese are—how can we say it?—Japanese after all, not Pakistanis, Burmese, Congolese, or Bolivians. To put it another way, the Indians, for example, can learn a good deal from the Japanese experience, but this does not mean that they are necessarily in a position to recapitulate it, any more than they can expect to emulate successfully the developmental evolution of the United States.

When one moves to Latin America, some different questions arise. Whereas the economic development maps of Africa and Asia are black with poverty, that of Latin America is mottled. Only a few countries, on the average, seem to display the same degree of poverty found in the other two continents. It is not surprising perhaps that Argentina and Uruguay, for example, have higher levels of living than most other Latin American countries and that Venezuela, with its huge petroleum production, ranks even higher; but the problem is more complicated than that.

Like most poorer countries, those in Latin America display a remarkable economic dualism between those economic activities like mining and beer production that are highly commercialized in terms of the world market, and those that are more nearly subsistence oriented. Whereas in many such countries the commercial sector is small relative to the other, in much of Latin America the commercial sector is relatively much larger and in this sense is more nearly analogous to the situation in Malaysia, for example, than to that in Indonesia or Burma. Perhaps another way to put it is that although most Latin Americans are abysmally poor, proportionally more are well-to-do. Much of their problem lies in the great chasm which seems to exist between the rich and the poor in given Latin American countries, as illustrated by the small size of the middle classes. A country like Colombia, for example, has a small middle class which, unlike the larger and mobile middle classes in the more highly developed countries of the world, does not bridge the gap between the "have-nots" and the "haves."

This point illustrates at least one of the limitations on the use of Gross National Product per Capita as a measure of economic development. It is, after all, an average, and it tells us very little about the distribution of income with a given country. It has other deficiencies, too. Calculations of GNP are usually made on the basis of values held in modern Western societies, but values differ from country to country, and so do the ways in which people spend their incomes. In some societies, a surplus of income over subsistence may go into savings or other forms of materially productive investment. In others, the apparent surplus may find its way to the tower of a Buddhist temple as a piece of gold leaf or may be spent on a wedding or funeral feast prescribed by local custom. Estimates of GNP also are based most often on the official exchange values of a given currency and not on its true purchasing power. This factor works both ways. On the one hand, if the official valuation is artificially high, it may mean a lower real GNP or real income, which is virtually the same thing. On the other, it may mean higher real income than is indicated, if price levels in a given country are particularly low. Finally, just as the use of GNP per capita for the United States obscures the existence of pockets of poverty in such places as Appalachia, so does it obscure the wide regional differences in income that appear in, say, Brazil, Chile, or Peru.

The geographer is interested in these regional differences *within* countries as well as those that appear to exist *between* countries. He is concerned with those differences in resource endowment and potentials that favor one such region or country over another; with the types of ecological relationships that bear upon the use of natural resources; with the functions of distance and transport costs that bear upon regional development and retardation; and with a better understanding of the role of great political and social movements, such as colonialism and nationalism, in the evolution of viable national and regional economies. In pursuit of these interests he does not, of course, work alone, nor should he. An understanding of the roots of poverty, and conversely of the touchstones for economic development to the extent that it can be attained at all, will be the product of all the social sciences working together on the comparative study of the "wealth of nations."

SUGGESTED READINGS

Buchanan, K., "Profiles of the Third World." *Pacific Viewpoint,* September 1964, 97–126.

Fryer, D. W., *World Economic Development.* New York: McGraw-Hill Book Company, 1965.

Ginsburg, N. S. (ed.), *Essays on Geography and Economic Development.* Chicago: University of Chicago, Research Paper No. 62, 1960.

Ginsburg, N. S. (ed.), *Atlas of Economic Development.* Chicago: University of Chicago Press, 1961.

13 RIVER BASIN PLANNING AND PEACE: THE LOWER MEKONG

Gilbert F. White

Rivers can be the raw nerves of contention among people living along their banks or they can be channels of peaceful cooperation. This is true of the more than one hundred streams that cut across international boundaries as well as of the thousands that rise and reach the sea within the area of a single country. For the allocation and development of fresh water for irrigation, navigation, municipal, power, or recreational needs can provoke intense rivalries, as among the riverine states along the lower Colorado River within the United States or in the Indus Basin whose waters drain from India into Pakistan. Generally, the international streams are slower to be developed because of the greater complications of getting more than one nation to cooperate.

To wisely manage a river to serve human needs is an exceedingly complex task. Properly done, it calls for a combination of political wisdom with judicious use of the best thought that natural sciences, social sciences, and engineering can marshal. At best, it must be carried out in ignorance of many of the consequences which will be triggered by river basin development. The difficulties, the challenges to scientific discovery, and the potentialities for building a peaceful world are nowhere better illustrated than in the Lower Mekong Basin of Southeast Asia.

Planning for the Lower Mekong is an experiment in human

manipulation of scientific and natural resources in a region which has been distinguished during the past nine years by severe international tensions, bitter guerilla warfare, and an unprecedented quality of international cooperation. The experiment might well collapse before tomorrow's dawn, so uncertain are its political supports, so tenuous its ties to established structures of public action and research. It involves the attempt of the four countries of Cambodia, Laos, Thailand, and South Vietnam to design a program for managing the waters of the basin. This is an area of about 300,000 square miles, larger than Texas, with a stream flow in excess of that of the Columbia River, and with large and appealing potentialities for management of water for irrigation, hydroelectric power, navigation, and flood control.

If the experiment abruptly ends, as it would if one of the four countries were to lose its ability to function governmentally as a result of civil strife, the experience might nevertheless yield valuable lessons in dealing with two of the pervasive problems affecting world peace. This is the problem of managing resources to meet the increasing needs of population, and the problem of living peacefully with marked disparity in developed resource endowment.

Although a few years ago the question of whether or not the world has sufficient natural resources to support prospective population might have been stated in terms of eagerly gauging the limited physical resource, we now are more inclined to put the problem in terms of finding effective social means of managing those resources of water, land, and energy that are known. The accelerated pace of technologic advance and the exciting promise of widely effective family planning have changed the problem, but have not reduced the difficulty of solution. The gap between technical knowledge and its practical application in field and stream and forest is progressively widening in most parts of the world, and it is becoming imperative to design new, more efficient, ways of bringing the instruments of science to the practical service of farmer, logger, fisherman, and miner.

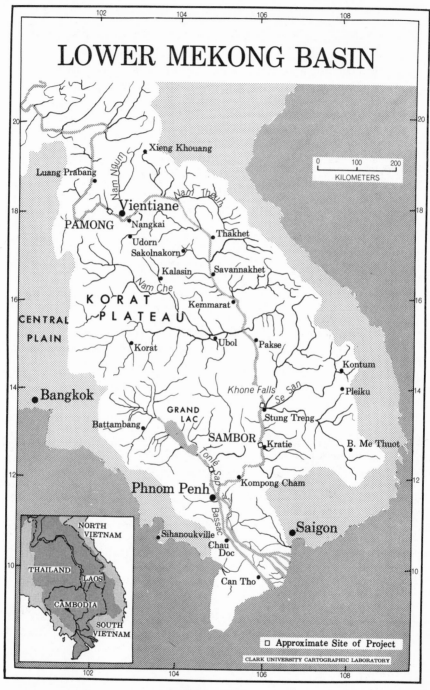

LOWER MEKONG BASIN

Xieng Khouang

Luang Prabang

Nam Ngum

Nam Theun

Vientiane

PAMONG

Nangkai

Udorn

Sakolnakorn

Thakhet

Kalasin

Savannakhet

Nam Che

KORAT
PLATEAU

Kemmarat

CENTRAL
PLAIN

Korat

Ubol

Pakse

Kontum

Bangkok

Khone Falls

Se San

Pleiku

GRAND
LAC

Battambang

Stung Treng

SAMBOR

Kratie

B. Me Thuot

Tonle Sap

Kompong Cham

Phnom Penh

Bassac

Saigon

Sihanoukville

Chau
Doc

Can Tho

| 0 | 100 | 200 |
KILOMETERS

NORTH
VIETNAM

THAILAND

LAOS

CAMBODIA

SOUTH
VIETNAM

□ **Approximate Site of Project**

CLARK UNIVERSITY CARTOGRAPHIC LABORATORY

Figure 13–1

At the same time, we face the prospect that even with application of technology on a wide front, at a rate as rapid as any of recent years, the absolute difference between the level of living in the high-income and low-income countries will widen for a long time to come. This mounting disparity will call for a degree of sustained ingenuity and generosity of spirit on the part of the well-endowed societies far exceeding anything displayed in the Marshall Plan, which was launched in 1948 by the United States to help Western Europe rehabilitate itself. For assistance must be given in a fashion that will eschew charitable beneficence or political patronage and will engage "haves" and "have nots" in a common cause.

If the experiment endures, the Lower Mekong would not only throw light on ways of solving these problems but it would be an instrument fashioning cooperation where distrust and violence now reign. It can hardly survive unless some more peaceful means of life is forged in the fire of Southeast Asian conflict.

It is possible, of course, that the Lower Mekong experiment could end without yielding either substantial evidence as to the effectiveness of the action taken or a framework for peaceful solutions. This is unlikely, for the experience to date already appears to have opened up new perspectives on the interlocking contributions of natural and social science in resource management on an international scale in a low-income area.

Throughout the basin—from rugged Laotian mountains where the river emerges from the high, narrow valley in which it traverses the Chinese plateaus, to the flat, alluvial soils of lower delta—water is one major key to economic growth. Its potentialities are barely recognized, for there is little systematic management of water outside of the fields where it falls as rain. This is an untamed river, so lightly touched by man that until comprehensive planning first was discussed in 1955 there were few grounds for either international conflict or agreement. The 1,700 miles of the main stream below the Chinese boundary are not as yet

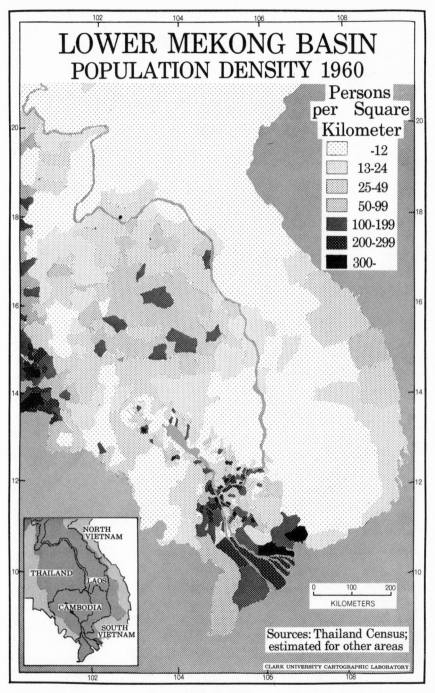

Figure 13–2

spanned by a single bridge. On the main stream there is not yet a major dam. The chief regulating works have been a small canal at Khone Falls, small dams and two large new dams in the Korat Plateau of Thailand, and navigation channels in the delta.

Most of the 20 million people of the basin live in the delta or in the Korat Plateau. Characteristically, they are rice farmers, and the towns are few in number. After the capital cities of Saigon, Phnom Penh, and Vientiane, there are only scattered urban centers along the river or in the plateau. The peasantry face great transformations as commercialized agriculture, urban growth, and transportation networks extend into the basin.

In the rugged uplands of Laos and South Vietnam, shifting cultivation is the prevailing way of life: the smoke of slash-and-burn clearing hangs heavy on the hills at the end of the dry season, and new fields are hacked out of the woodland every three to five years. In the alluvial soils of the valley bottoms, rice can be grown year after year but only in the wet season and it is subject to damage from drought and flood. The wooded interfluves are grazed when grass permits and are subject to severe degradation of both vegetation and soil. The alluvial lands of the lower river and delta are cultivated in the face of high water table, annual flooding, and saline intrusions up the distributary channels. Here the balance of stream flow, ground-water level, and water quality is extremely delicate.

Although statistics for parts of the basin outside Thailand are sketchy at best, a few rough estimates can be made as to future needs. Total population may be expected, at the present growth rates, to double by 1985. If this occurs and if a modest increase in level of living for the enlarged population is to be achieved, agricultural production must grow at a rate of about 3.5 to 4 per cent annually, and manufacturing production at a rate of about 6 to 7 per cent. These are high goals and, while such rates have been attained in some parts of the world, they are immensely difficult to sustain.

Attempts by the four Mekong countries to reach these rates of growth call for a judicious allocation of resources in national programs that will involve education, trade promotion, and a large arsenal of measures to increase production efficiency. In these efforts, water management can play an important role, but it is not necessarily the most significant measure at a particular time and place. For example, fertilizer improvement might promise earlier and more certain returns on investment than would irrigation in many sectors of the basin.

Water management would assist in at least five ways. The provision of water for irrigation would permit growing a second crop of rice during the dry season and this, in turn, might encourage diversification of crops and stabilization of forest and pasture use in adjacent areas. Water would be substituted for fire as an instrument of land management. Second, generation of low-cost electric power could support the growth of an industrial complex on a modest scale and of smaller commercial centers. Third, improvement of river transport facilities in conjunction with road programs could stimulate the commercialization of the basin and the development of specialized production. Fourth, fishing could be enlarged in both stream and lake. Fifth, the disrupting effects of floods could be reduced by a combination of forecasting, structural adjustments, and flow control.

These possibilities are stated in the conditional tense because staggering obstacles stand in the way of realization of any of them. As resource development schemes around the world so painfully testify, there is many a failure between technical plan and human realization. A basic obstacle is the lack of scientific information as to the full consequences of tampering with any part of the hydrologic cycle. A small reservoir intended to increase agricultural output may fail to do so because canals to the dry lands are not properly constructed, or because inadequate drainage leads to early waterlogging and salting, or because of lack of needed credit, extension, or marketing services. The information essential to sound plans includes not only the basis for correct structural and hydrologic design but also clear recognition of the steps involved in assuring that available water will be transformed into increased production: these steps would draw on analysis of economic and social organization and value systems of the communities involved.

Notwithstanding political pressures to get under way with earthmoving equipment, the committee of the four countries decided, upon its organization in 1957, to concentrate initially on basic studies to supply some of this information. Then arose the obstacle of coordinating the studies from a score of different disciplines in an international structure. The realistic diplomats and engineers said it would be impossibly ponderous and complex. A few studies began. Today, they comprise the expenditure of more than $30 million and the contributions of twenty additional nations and eleven international agencies. In a wholly unprecedented integration of scientific and technical units, the basic elements of design are being fashioned.

A team of Indian engineers uses the results of field reconnaissance survey by a Japanese group, draws on maps prepared by Filipinos from Canadian air photos, and applies Australian damsite geological investigations, hydrologic measurements by Americans, and French soil surveys. Slowly, an understanding of the basin's intricacies is gained; and a few specific projects have reached the construction stage.

Here, another obstacle appears. A multiple-purpose power, irrigation, and flood control dam can be launched in Thailand under West German financing with some sense of security in the investment. In Laos and South Vietnam, the presence of military conflict and the dangers of collapse of civilian administration are so great as to make a construction or village improvement program seem futile. In Cambodia, the government is supersensitive to foreign entanglements. Throughout the delta, terror nightly stalks when the sun sinks on the little bamboo and mud forts.

Many observers in 1965 say it is soft-headed to talk about anything more in the Lower Mekong until the area is pacified, but the work continues to go forward. Indeed, the fact of constructive cooperation may be an aid to resolving the conflict.

Returning to the basic need to manage resources so as to meet population needs and to deal harmoniously with disparity in way of life, three problems are raised acutely by the Lower Mekong adventure. The first is the question of how refined an analysis is needed and can be sustained by resource development planning in a low-income country. The second is whether or not it is practicable to carry out refined and integrated planning on an international basis. The third is the extent to which such planning can support rather than impede international cooperation and stability. Principal attention will be directed to the first question.

It has been common for a long time for engineers and hydrologists to advise against the construction of water resources management works—the great dams on American, Soviet, and Chinese rivers—until there has been adequate collection of basic hydrologic, geologic, and soils data and until there has been sufficient time for thoughtful selection of the most appropriate design. Oftentimes this prudence has been violated in the vigorous search by governments under popular pressure to show early action in the form of earth-moving and concrete monuments and flowing water in deep canals. The persistent question in the minds of technicians and politicians becomes, "how much knowledge of what kind do we need before we start work?"

Essentially, water management is the art of so changing the flow and quality of water as to effect the flow and quality of silt and organisms in those two main physical systems related to the hydrologic cycle, and so as directly or through those subsidiary changes to effect flow of income and of goods in the area affected by the water works. A dam on the Middle Mekong will profoundly affect the movement of silt in the channels downstream, will influence the fish and plant life in those same waters, and

195

may be the instrument by which the way of life of farmers in the flood plain and in the adjoining areas under the command of irrigation ditches may be basically altered.

When it is assumed that the construction of a small reservoir in the Lower Mekong will lead automatically to an improvement in irrigation agriculture in the area, there may be no opportunity to make scientific inquiry as to the relationships that will be affected. Without detailed studies as to how and where the water would be applied to what soils in what system of farming in what cultural circumstances, it may be that within a few years after the completion of a reservoir a lack of results not only will demonstrate failure of the project but failure of man to specify the natural relationships he would like to command.

In the case of the Lower Mekong, more explicit attention was given to certain social and economic aspects of design in the project activity than in most resource management schemes around the world. This is not to conclude that the attention was in any sense comprehensive, but it is to say that important questions were asked and that some attempts were made to answer them. Geographic analysis was used in the formulation of priorities and study programs. More will be required. Inevitably, heavier emphasis was placed upon engineering and physical investigations than on social investigations or upon tracing the ecological effects of proposed work. A few comprehensive river programs in the United States and the Soviet Union have attempted to deal with as broad a range of questions in connection with major work. One of the pioneering efforts in that direction was headed by the American geographer, Barrows, in the Upper Columbia Basin at the time the Grand Coulee Dam was under construction. Later research has helped increase our capacity to predict what will be the consequences of such measures as reducing flood elevations or irrigating dry land or altering stream regimen. Increasingly, attention is turned toward the careful appraisal of alternative ways of reaching desired human goals.

Can we realistically expect national and international agencies to work together in using the results of many scientific disciplines in as complex an operation as that involved in resource management in a basin the size of the Lower Mekong? Are the difficulties so massive that we cannot, with our existing instruments of government, hope to deal with them through a loosely constructed international agency? So far, the Lower Mekong experiment suggests that it is not impossible both to plan and carry out many basic investigations with such a mechanism. It is clear that a competent staff is necessary and that a peculiar genius of leadership is invaluable.

Can the struggle to maintain and manage nature's riches provide a framework for a political organization which otherwise might not be viable? Again, the Lower Mekong experiment is not conclusive, but it does show that even in an area of intense political stress it is possible to work out fairly practicable relations over a period of nine years. From the Lower Mekong experience comes recognition that the concept of large-scale international collaboration to deal with the management of nature on a regional basis may have sufficient appeal to both the technical and the political mind to support a kind of enterprise which could not survive in an atmosphere of sticky economic and political negotiations.

If we are to live fruitfully in a world where disparity seems bound to prevail for generations to come, we must cultivate earthy, concrete ways in which high-income and low-income nations can harmoniously collaborate to close the gap. Insofar as natural resource development is needed, the effort calls for combining the best of the world's scientific knowledge in plans that forward-looking indigenous governments help frame and for which they will take responsibility. The method of helping both in studies and in action should promote scientific competence and practical wisdom without sacrificing local dignity and self-regard. This is the promise that is held out by ventures which are taking shape in the Senegal and Chad basins in Africa, and in parts of

South America and where, hopefully, absence of strife and tension will not serve to deflect international attention from needs equally as pressing as those of the Lower Mekong.

It may be that the enterprises most likely to yield early and sound returns are those which tackle restricted problems in single countries with a minimum of international machinery. However, the Lower Mekong experience to date shows that it is possible for more complex problems to be attacked by an international team without yet collapsing under its own weight. Perhaps the lesson here is that a powerful ingredient in the momentous drive to improve the management of world resources lying ahead of us is a vision of the challenge that integrated development presents, a vision of cooperation of the world's intellectual communities toward concrete goals. Regardless of the immediate fate of the Lower Mekong, the quality of that vision may be a means of mobilizing scientific and administrative resources for tasks that otherwise would be long delayed if seen in a narrower framework. In basic probing of the earth's skin and in the homely arts of handling water, soil, and vegetation may lie one powerful tool for organizing intellectual forces in the pursuit of peace.

SUGGESTED READINGS

Ackerman, E. A., and Lof, G. O. G., *Technology in American Water Development*. Baltimore: Johns Hopkins Press, 1959.

Farmer, B. H., *Pioneer Colonization in Ceylon*. London: Oxford University Press, 1957.

Fifield, R. H., and Schaaf, C. H., *The Lower Mekong*. New York: D. Van Nostrand, 1963.

Furon, R., *Le Problème de l'Eau dans le Monde*. Paris: Payot, 1963.

Hirshleifer, J., DeHaven, J. C., and Milliman, J. W., *Water Supply: Economics, Technology, and Policy*. Chicago: University of Chicago Press, 1960.

Jarrett, H. (ed.), *Comparisons in Resource Management*. Baltimore: Johns Hopkins Press, 1961.

Landsberg, H. H., *Natural Resources for U.S. Growth*. Baltimore: Johns Hopkins Press, 1964.

Leopold, L., and Longbein, W. B., *A Primer on Water*. Washington, D.C.: U. S. Government Printing Office, 1960.

Michael, H. P. (ed.), *Water Development in Less Developed Areas*. Berlin: Duncker and Humblot, 1965.

United Nations, *Integrated River Basin Development: Report by a Panel of Experts*. New York: United Nations, 1958.

White, G. F., *Science and the Future of Arid Lands*. Paris: UNESCO, 1961.

White, G. F., "The Mekong River Plan," *Scientific American*, April 1963, 49–60.

14 GEOGRAPHY AND THE DEVELOPMENT OF PEASANT AGRICULTURE

James M. Blaut

Most of the world's population lives on farms, and most of these are peasant farms. Here is one very good reason why geographers, and their fellow scientists, devote so much attention to the study of peasant farms and farmers. But there is another reason, more urgent than the first. We are now in an "age of development," which aims to bring about a rapid increase in the per capita income and food supply of underdeveloped countries. In most of these countries, peasant farming is the prime source of food, the principal occupation, and indeed the major geographic, economic, and social sector. Yet, most peasant farmers are still as poor as ever, and per capita food supply seems even to be declining. These are not, therefore, "developing countries." We might better describe them as countries which are striving to unlock the doors to development, but have not thus far discovered the key. Discovering things is a job which sciences like geography are rather good at, and the study of peasant agriculture is an important part of their quest.

Just how geographers go about the study of peasant agriculture, and how their findings can assist in bringing about its development, are the main themes of this essay. Notice, however, that I say "can assist" instead of "has assisted." Thus far, the contribution of geography to peasant development programs has been rather meager, and mostly unsolicited. The same holds true in varying degrees for all the sciences concerned with peasant farms and farmers. At the same time, the development programs themselves have not achieved any widespread and notable success. The question then arises: does the one fact explain the other? Does scientific ignorance about peasant farming provide a sufficient reason (although not the only reason) for lack of development? And do sciences like geography have knowledge available but unapplied? Clearly, these questions should be considered first, if a discussion of the usefulness of geographic knowledge is to have any practical value.

SCIENTIFIC IGNORANCE

When the age of development began, some two decades ago, the improvement of peasant agriculture was believed to be a straightforward and relatively simple affair. Needless to say, this belief proved to be unjustified: farm earnings have not increased in most underdeveloped countries, and food supplies are now decreasing. The bases for this belief were, on the one hand, a perfectly laudable wish for rapid (and inexpensive) progress and, on the other hand, a comfortably wish-fulfilling theory of development. Perhaps we should not call this latter a theory; it was actually an assemblage of half-formed notions about peasant agriculture and underdeveloped economies, the whole cemented by optimism, not evidence, since science at that time knew very little about such matters. This might be called the "tropicalizing" theory of agricultural development, analogous to that minor modification which is performed on cold-climate raincoats, radios, automobiles, and the like, to adapt them for sale in tropical countries. Manufacturers "tropicalize" an existing product to save the research costs, development time, and special facilities involved in fashioning a totally new product or range of products, one for each country. But the item must, of course, be adaptable in the first place: one would not attempt to modify a pair of snowshoes, say, or long woolen underwear.

The analogy to agricultural development is quite direct. The "tropicalizing" theory presupposes adaptability of two things: advanced—that is, post-development—traits of Western agriculture; and the techniques for generating agricultural changes which were successfully used in the Western development process. Adaptability here implies detachability and reattachability for farming traits and development techniques. It is doubtful that anyone believed in the absurdity that peasant cultures in Asia, Africa, and Latin America were identical in values and social organization with the ninteenth-century peasantry of Europe or North America. However, those who purveyed the "tropicalizing" theory did, indeed, believe that all the important traits which had been acquired by Western agriculture as benefits of development, along with the techniques which had brought about that development, could be detached from their Western cultural matrix; then, as it were, be shipped east (or south); and finally, be reattached to peasant cultures. All of this, it was presumed, would save immense amounts of time and money otherwise needed for research and development, and would permit the use of the existing plant—notably the educational and research plant—exactly as in the case of any "tropicalized" product.

Unfortunately, the theory had one fatal flaw: the traits and techniques were not all that easy to adapt. They were detachable —as evidence, the eastward and southward migration of experts and implements—but not reattachable. And this flaw was traceable to the unsupported notions about peasant agriculture mentioned previously. We did not know enough about peasant economy and society. We did not know that the best farmers, being also the biggest farmers, may not be the natural leaders (in contravention of perhaps the oldest principle in Western farm economics). We did not know enough about tropical soils and did not anticipate that high-yielding crop varieties may come to grief on low-nutrient soils. We did not, for that matter, know enough about peasant geography: for example, that new crops may be worthless if they cannot be eaten and no roads lead out of the area; or that mechanization may not make sense in a one-acre market garden; or that soil conservation may not be practiced if soil erosion is not perceived by the farmers.

The blame for failure does not fall on Western techniques, Western experts, or Western-trained agricultural officers. If a visiting expert is allowed only six months in which to effect an improvement, he has no choice but to "tropicalize" some known and proven trait. If the research arm of a department of agriculture lacks the budget for photogrammatic and soil surveys, new experiment stations, specialist officers, farm management and rural community studies, and the like, it must content itself with less costly exercises, such as crop, fertilizer, and pesticide trials; it must, in other words, "tropicalize." If indeed there is any blame at all, it attaches to the sciences themselves, for allowing an unsupported and unsanctioned theory to gain such currency and influence, and to those planners whose enthusiasm for progress made them all too willing to accept an unfounded theory promising quick, cheap development without the pains and frustrations of basic research.

Agricultural development is neither quick nor cheap, and overoptimism has given way to various shades of pessimism. The most pessimistic view of all, and in some circles the most popular, holds that peasant farming simply cannot be improved, at least in our time; that agricultural development efforts must be detoured around the existing peasant farms and redirected: into major reclamation projects of the dam-building, ditch-digging, and land-clearing variety; into large-scale corporate or state farms; and into industry—this last having the indirect aim of paying for imported food and absorbing the supposedly surplus peasants. But disillusionment alone does not justify this degree of pessimism.

For one thing, not enough time has been given the past and present efforts at developing peasant agriculture to judge their ultimate effect. For another, the alternatives have not proven wildly successful either, least of all in those countries where peasant farming predominates as the major source of food and employment, as, in most underdeveloped countries, it does.

In fact, the popularity of this view is a reflection less of experience with peasant programs than of changes which are taking place in the ideology and politics of economic development as a whole. For one thing, development is becoming institutionalized; it is acquiring the flavor of a normal governmental (and intergovernmental) function, and this implies a somewhat heightened sensitivity to political and economic power. Peasants in most countries seem to have little of either. Investment in peasant agriculture does not prevent *coups d'état* (although it may obviate revolution). It offers very few plums to the larger private interests —manufacturing, banking, construction, wholesaling, and landowning—and indeed offers a direct threat to some of them. And it does not produce monuments, like dams, factories, and housing projects, which have political and fiscal utility, even when unused. For another thing, economic development is becoming professionalized—by which I mean that a corpus of professional experts in development planning is emerging, both in national planning boards and in supranational agencies. This should, in theory, be highly advantageous for agricultural development. Not so, however, if the experts in question are recruited from an urban elite, given training in architecture, civil engineering, or industrial management, perhaps given advanced training in urban design or macro-economics, and then, finally, given the task of allocating investment as between agriculture, on the one hand, and industry, ports, housing projects, and multipurpose dams, on the other. Such folk may not always allocate to the peasant sector its proper share of resources—or indeed of optimism.

A belief system may arise out of hopes or fears, but it must nevertheless be credible. It needs a sustaining theory, scientific or seemingly so. This held true in the case of earlier optimism about peasant development, and it holds true even more for the current pessimism—even more, because some scientific data, at least, have been built into the latter. These data are for the most part, and unsurprisingly, the findings from official or informal studies of unsuccessful programs, of newly discovered obstacles to development, and of macro-economic magnitudes in which the peasant sector provides one statistic—by no means the best one—among many. Out of these data has emerged an array of postulates which offer one or another explanation for the failure of development programs. To these are added a single cementing theory which converts any postulate explaining lack of past success into one asserting the certainty of future failure. I call this—tongue very deeply in cheek—the "mysterious tropical malady theory," because it postulates, in its purest and most extreme form, that peasant farming has within it some toxic factor, unknown and incurable, which must inevitably attack any peasant development program and in the end defeat it.

One of the postulates behind this theory, somewhat anthropological although disowned by anthropologists, asserts the existence of impenetrable cultural barriers—as though peasant cultures erect barriers while other cultures do not; and as though development programs are bound to fail even when noneconomic facets of culture are properly taken into account. Another asserts that peasant farmers are motivated by social, not economic, values, and are therefore unresponsive to the economic lures of development—as though social values are ever, in any culture, separable from economic values; and as though the quest for food is an economic value in one culture and a social value in another. Still another postulates what is called a backward-sloping labor supply curve for peasant farmers, implying in effect that these farmers work harder when the incentives are less and vice versa—which is untrue. And so on with other beliefs about lack of achievement motivation, immobilization of land through joint ownership, suppression of the entrepreneurial spirit in extended peasant families, and the like.

Not all of these propositions assert the impossibility of genuine peasant development; most, indeed, imply only that development will be a difficult and costly task. But converting them into a theory of nondevelopment is a simple matter: just project past failure into the future. And this is what many national and supranational agencies have done. The result is even more failure: a defeatist theory tends to fulfill its own defeatist prophecies.

SCIENTIFIC KNOWLEDGE

Today we know a great deal more about peasant farming than we did at the close of World War II. Granted, the emphasis placed on research in connection with development programs remains as disproportionately low as ever. But scientific knowledge is, after all, cumulative—a point worth stressing to those who allocate development funds. Perhaps the day is not far off when ignorance about peasant farming will no longer serve as an excuse for failure. Certainly the day has passed when scientific ignorance offered *laissez passer* to exaggerated optimism or pessimism about the development potential of peasant farming.

Knowledge of peasant agriculture has increased in quite a normal, scientific way, beginning long before World War II, with descriptions of peasant areas and communities, by geographers, anthropologists, and others, and with a small number of intensive studies in these fields and such others as farm economics, rural sociology, soil science, and, most notably, agricultural botany. (The last-named had its respectable tradition of crop diffusion and adaptation, carried out by the botanic gardens, plant explorers, and of course peasants.) But, in 1945, the available infor-

mation was too meager to be of much use in development programs. Since then, however, each field has accumulated an
impressive number of detailed studies in many peasant areas.
The number is impressive, however, only if one's perspective is
world-wide; no one country has assembled enough information
in each of the critical fields—soils, hydrology, climatology, botany, zoology, anthropology, rural sociology, agricultural economics, geography, and so on—to achieve an adequate research
base for peasant development.

The present state of our knowledge about peasant agriculture
can be summed up fairly simply—bearing in mind that the subject is grossly interdisciplinary, and that one cannot really add up
the knowledge of many disciplines to find an average. The kind of
summary I have in mind is a model, or idealized concept, of the
peasant farm, and another of the total farming milieu. Recall
that, in 1945, the prevailing models of peasant agriculture were
essentially simple analogies to the, by then, well-known agricultural forms of temperate, Western areas. The analogies were
thought to be so close that parts were interchangeble: thus, machinery, credit devices, and the like, could be fitted into the
peasant farm as a kind of replacement part. The same would hold
true for macro-economic elements, such as marketing methods.
The parts did not, however, fit. The accumulation of knowledge
since then has altered the farm and farming-region models in two
fundamental ways. First of all, each new bit of information has
supplanted some poorly fitting part—or, for those who preferred
to admit ignorance, some previously missing part. By now, we
have a complete model of the ideal-typical peasant farm and region. The model is still too general to serve as a "how-to-do-it"
schema for development agencies. But it is complete, and therefore perfectly adequate as a "how-*not*-to-do-it" schema—a kind of
pilot's preflight check list, designed to prevent failure through
oversight. Second of all, we now know that one model of the farm
and one of the farming region will not suffice: there are many

kinds of peasant farms, peasant societies, peasant economies, and peasant regions; peasant farming is, in fact, the most varied of all categories of agricultural systems.

One can proceed in the same way to summarize the present state of our ignorance, which is particularly acute in two areas. First of all, since peasant farming comprises a multiplicity of types, a model must be elaborated for each one, with enough detail to fill in each critical trait of society, economy, and environment; understanding the nature of the particular, local type— not simply of peasant agriculture in general—is the requirement for effecting change in that type. The same holds true for models of the total farming region, where types as such are rather obscure; where, accordingly, the traits of the individual region—its soils, hydrology, communication lines, and the like—must be known. So the problem at both levels is exceedingly complex, and requires painstaking, local research—the majority of which, in most countries, has not yet been carried out.

The second area of ignorance is a matter less of traits than of systems. The farm is a total system—in a sense, an entity, the parts of which interweave into a functioning whole. This is true also of the region. Understanding the parts does not give us the needed knowledge of the whole, unless we understand also the relations between these parts, the way, for example, a farmer's perception of soils affects his behavior in regard to soil conservation. The problem of examining and cataloguing traits as such, including traits of economy, society, and environment, is a task for the specialist sciences like agricultural economics and entomology. The problem of putting these traits together into a whole, functional system model is a task for a rather different group of sciences, one member of which is cultural geography. And so we come to what is the main theme of this chapter: the role of cultural geography in the study and development of peasant agriculture.

GEOGRAPHIC KNOWLEDGE

Cultural geographers concern themselves mainly with the way human beings use their natural resources—the way they produce food, build houses and roads, circulate products, migrate, and the like. All of these questions come under the heading of resource-utilization, "land-use" for short. Geographers study land-use in the context of a particular region, which is defined in most cases as a physical area occupied by a specific social or cultural unit. The unit may be a nation, a language group, a community, or even a single farm. A farm, after all, is a specific social unit of one culture making use of a definite piece of land. A farm is therefore a basic building-block of land utilization.

Any region, whether it is a single farm or an entire province or country, is what we think of as a land-use system. It is an organized complex of parts which interrelate with one another so that a change in any one of the parts affects all the others, and, of course, the system as a whole. The system has boundaries, or at least boundary processes, and any influence entering the system from outside will also produce reverberating changes in the system as a whole, and in its parts. A land-use system is an exceedingly complex entity. Its parts include the elements of society and economy; also material artifacts, such as houses and crops; and also each of the natural elements: soil, climate, land forms, water, and vegetation. This leads into a general and very informal theory of land-use systems, which states basically that a change in any one part of the system, for example, economic growth or soil erosion, will alter the total system in predictable ways; and that the same will occur if some external change impinges—if, for example, world prices drop, or a hurricane strikes. The concept of land-use as an organized system applies to the individual farm as it does to a larger region. It therefore provides a general concept or model of the farm as a total geographic entity, containing both cultural and natural parts, and this is of course a much more comprehensive perspective than, say, an economic or social model.

On any farm, the major land-use elements are the following: first, the physical resources, the land; second, an arsenal of tools, machines, buildings, vehicles, crops, livestock, seed, and fertilizers; third, a social group, the farm family or some other organized force which applies its labor to the tools and resources; fourth, a corpus of values, or attitudes, or goals, which the group or parts of the group hold in common; fifth, a body of technological knowledge about resource-using techniques and the resources themselves, a field of perception and memory which lends meaning, relevance, and accessibility to the resources; and finally, a set of decisions governing the way a group behaves toward its perceived and valuated resources, and defining the decision-field within which this behavior retains its efficacy. These are traits of all land-use systems of the class "farms." They add up to much more than a trait list, however: they describe a total system model in which the traits themselves are integrated together into a whole. This whole has persistence, locality (although it is movable), and boundaries (although these may be highly permeable).

The farm is also the locus of an economic system, a social system, an ecological system (if not precisely an eco-system), and others. The land-use system articulates with each of these: economizing is applied to resources; social values are applied to land-using behavior (weeding after all being a function of weeds). But the single, comprehensive system which governs the processes of producing, consuming, constructing, and traversing material resources is the land-use system. Social, economic, and habitat relations are, from the standpoint of this system, boundary processes.

The geographer studies agricultural land-use at quite a number of levels. He studies the farm and type of farm as a single system. He studies the individual land-use trait in isolation, as a distributed and diffusing phenomenon. He studies the farm as one element, or cell, in the larger organism, or regional system, which may be a village, valley, province, or nation. There are thus two rather broad methods of analysis, comparable in a way to the two views one gets through either end of a telescope. One focuses on the individual farm or, at most, village, as a primary system, and analyzes its components in terms of functional interrelations and structural position (with emphasis on the functional). From this, an ideal concept or system model for the type of farm is evolved, tracing the evolution, differentiation, and distribution of the farm, describing, explaining, and predicting its variability in relation to varying cultural and physical conditions, and fitting it as a unit into the spatially larger system. This approach we call microgeographic. The other approach, that of macrogeography, focuses on the larger farming region as such. The individual farm or village, in this approach, is a component or part. There are other kinds of components as well: local microsystems such as markets, quarries, shophouses, and the like; and region-wide microsystems (called subsystems) such as road nets and extension services. But the larger the region, the more complex; the more complex, the more unique. Thus macrogeographic regional systems tend to be one or few of a kind, and the analytic procedure involves either close study of the individual system in historical, spatial-structural, and functional terms, or comparative analysis of the subsystems, such as marketing and communication nets. In contrast to the microgeographic approach, the macrogeographic is on the whole more quantitative and precise. It is less capable, however, of generalization, and therefore theory. Theory of the farm, not the farming region, will be the first to emerge.

Every farm differs to some extent from every other farm, and one can, in theory, develop as many system models as there are individual farms in the world. Or, one can be satisfied with a single, general model covering all variations. Or, one can classify farms according to any of countless combinations of criteria, and use a single model to describe each class. Peasant farming is obviously in some sense a class or type of farm, so the third approach is the one needed in developing an analytic model for the class "peasant farms." But here we encounter a real problem. Is there some natural basis for classification, some obvious set of cleavage planes according to which peasant farming emerges as a clearly distinguishable type? This seems to be the case, for two reasons: First, the criteria for differentiation of peasant farming emerge directly from the set of elements mentioned previously as standard parts of any farming-system model: values; technical skill and knowledge, including resource perception; labor; productive material culture; and utilized resources, or land. The category of "decisions" is viewed as an essentially dependent variable, and therefore a residual. Second, for each of the differentiating elements, one finds either qualitative cleavages between subclasses— for example, between sugar cane, with its arsenal of associated material culture, and mixed root-crop farming. Of course, one can divide any element into as many subclasses as one wishes.

Every unit-system is a part of some larger system, rather as a cell is a part of the organism. From this flows a pragmatic rule: the more open the system, the less useful the study—or, the more useful it is to move up to the next higher level, that of the superordinate system. This, in agricultural geography, is the rule one uses to decide between the microgeographic and macrogeographic strategies, the study of individual farms and villages or the study of macroregions and nations. In the case of peasant agriculture, this rule is particularly crucial. Recall that great stress has been laid here on the fact that peasant farming is not a relatively closed system, not autarkic, like, for example, shifting cultivation in the deeper forests of Borneo and hacienda agriculture in the farthest corners of South America.

Peasant farming lies midway between autarky and commercialization, and does so for an important historical reason, which is well brought out in Eric Wolf's recent volume, *Peasants* (Englewood, N.J.: Prentice-Hall, 1966). Wolf shows that a peasantry emerged when a level of sociocultural integration higher than the village first appeared. This was when the earliest states, and estates, developed to the point where sufficient power could be applied to force the autarkic village, and the individual family farm, to deliver up a portion of its produce in the form of taxes or rent. In terms of historical geography, one can describe this process—millennias old—as an opening up of the microgeographic farm and village systems and a concretization of the farming macroregion. In other words, until one has a partially coherent macroregion, one does not have peasant agriculture. The more coherent the former, the more the latter comes to resemble commercial family farming, and to follow the laws of Von Thünen and the market. Indeed, our failure to view peasant agriculture as an open system, and our failure to pay adequate attention to macroregional patterns, such as marketing and land tenure, is one rather important reason for our failure to bring about peasant development.

If we were concerned here with the problem of developing a general-purpose geographic classification of farming systems, we might proceed as follows: First, divide the social subsystem (the element of labor into two minimal classes, "family-sized" and "large-scale." Second, divide the subsystem or element of values, on the basis of overall purpose of production, into three classes: "autarkic" (or "subsistence"—a somewhat ambiguous word), "semi-commercial" (when more than half the output is sold or otherwise delivered across the system boundary, but less than half the inputs are imported), and "commercial." Third, divide the material-culture element—tools and products—into the sixteen classes based on significant presence or absence of ground crops, tree crops, livestock, and labor-saving devices. Fourth, divide the element of land into the four crop-ecological classes based on significant presence or absence of man-made improvements in the chemical and physical environment, respectively, of crop (and feed) plants. Fifth, set aside the element of technological knowledge and perception on grounds that our data are almost wholly absent, although known technique is almost always significantly broader than the actual, utilized technique associated with material culture and crop ecology. The output is 360 separate classes or cells, of which perhaps 25 per cent have significant membership. Notice that external, nonsystem factors, such as climate and marketing method, are rigidly excluded from the classification—which is, after all, a classification only of farms.

But our concern is with peasant farming alone. Here we have surprisingly few problems of definition. A peasant farm is a land-use system in which the social group involved is a single family, nuclear or extended. What distinguishes it from commercial family farms is a set of values: a peasant farm is operated principally to provide for the needs of the family—that is, for disposal—within the boundaries of the system itself. This does not mean autarkic production. It means, first of all, that emphasis will be placed on food production, so that products can be consumed if it turns out that no market exists for sale (or if taxes and rent are not collected). Secondly, it means that, however much of the production is sold, very little of what we call the farm inputs will be purchased for cash; nearly all of the materials and labor needed for production, in other words, comes either from the farm itself or from loan, gift, barter exchange, or reciprocal labor exchange within a village or community. One important corollary of this feature is the fact that peasant farmers are not likely to make use of new technology, including machines and commercial fertilizers, if such factors must be purchased. Therefore, since most factors of this sort cannot normally be acquired except by purchase, peasant farms tend to maintain a fairly low level of actual technology. Stated differently, peasant farmers are not "technologically ignorant" as some authorities suppose; on the contrary, they have in most cases achieved an extraordinarily high level of proficiency in utilizing available labor and materials, given the prevailing constraints of land, food habits, rent, and taxes. And their technical knowledge is always at a higher level still. Indeed, as Theodore Schultz points out in his excellent volume, *Transforming Traditional Agriculture* (New Haven, Conn.: Yale University Press, 1964), there is even a rather large stock of material capital on most peasant farms—if one measures it in terms of labor cost, not cash cost.

Peasant farming must be distinguished from several other types of family farm as well as from the commercialized varieties. In small and relatively closed societies, usually in some senses primitive and tribal, very little production seeps out of the farming community. Here one can speak of very nearly pure autarky or subsistence agriculture, although the community, not the family farm, is likely to be the autarky unit, the half-closed system. In areas dominated by large commercial plantations or sharecropped estates, as in many parts of the West Indies, the family farm is not likely to be a peasant farm, since the principal production and marketing decisions are made by the estate, which may also own and control the land and much of the productive material culture. Often such a family farm is merely one segment of the estate's decision-field, and not really a farm at all. Finally, in those areas where special marketing advantages have led peasant farms to become largely or totally commercialized, as in the case of Chinese market-gardeners in Southeast Asia, one can record an instance of evolution beyond peasant agriculture.

Peasant farming, therefore, derives its uniqueness as a category from a combination of two characteristics which distinguish it from other types of family farming: values and productive material culture. In a general-purpose classification of farming systems it occupies those cells formed by the intersection of "family-sized farming," "semi-autarky," and "absence of significant labor-saving devices" (beyond the bullock and water wheel). It is not unique in other respects. For instance, land itself, or natural endowment, has little to do with the case. Peasant farms are found in all or nearly all of the major environments of the world, although the progress of commercialization in the United States and collectivization in the Soviet Union and China in recent times has tended to squeeze peasant farming out of most midlatitude areas, and limit its distribution mainly to tropical and subtropical areas. But peasant farms can, in fact, occupy almost any environment permitting agriculture. And by and large, they do so. This is important in itself. Peasant farming can adapt itself to a wider range of environments than any commercial farming system, with the single exception of range grazing—which produces much less food per acre. This adaptability is perhaps the strongest point in favor of peasant farming, and its best defense against replacement by other systems.

Similarly, there are no distinctive types of crop or livestock which are peculiar to peasant agriculture, and there are very few varieties that are *not* grown by peasants. The only common feature is a very strong emphasis on food crops and, in most areas, a relatively slight emphasis on animals. Each culture has its own food preferences, of course, and this is reflected in the great variety of crops and stock to be found on peasant farms around the world.

GEOGRAPHIC KNOWLEDGE APPLIED

Thus far, a very general picture or model of the peasant farm as a geographic entity, or total land-use system, has been presented. There are benefits to be gained from looking at the farm in this comprehensive way. First, attention can be paid to the interrelations among very different characteristics, thus avoiding what is perhaps the worst mistake of all in agricultural policy: to assume that the only way to change some one undesirable characteristic of a farm is to attack that characteristic directly. For instance, efforts have been made time and again to persuade peasant farmers to adopt a wide range of technological innovations designed to increase food production, and usually without much success. Quite often, the farmers who refuse to adopt the innovation are simply called ignorant, or conservative, or else it is assumed that they are not acting according to so-called rational economic motives. But when the adoption of new technology requires, as it usually does, a heavy outlay of cash, this conflicts directly with a basic peasant-farming value which dictates that production inputs should not be purchased if a serious risk to the farm would result. Therefore, in the great majority of cases, peasant farmers are probably aware of the benefits of the new technique but do not dare try it. Obviously, the worst approach in such a situation would be to insist, by such means as education and agricultural extension, that farmers really ought to adopt the technique: they will not respond. It would be much better either to improve the marketing system so that cash flows more freely through the farm system, or to provide capital loans without requiring mortgage security, or both. In other words, since various factors are interrelated, one can be changed by getting at it through another. What has been said is closely analogous to the arguments of those anthropologists and sociologists who remind us constantly that a new technique will not gain acceptance if it comes into conflict with some basic social value, or some important element of social or religious organization. The present discussion, however, deals with interrelations among elements within the land-use system itself, not between land-use elements and other traits of culture. Certain values, roles, and social-organizational structures are bound up in the land-use system; others are not.

There can be major benefits in using this geographic approach to peasant farming as a land-use system. In taking a diagnostic look at any human or biological system as a whole, instead of focusing narrowly on one or several of its parts, trouble spots within the system can be more readily identified. Biologists sometimes call these the limiting factors. Some geographers prefer the term "tension points." The essential principle is this: when a system is not functioning properly, usually one or a few properties are responsible; these are the limiting factors. Other properties are of course affected, but these are merely symptoms. In this context, a tension point or limiting factor in peasant farming is whatever tends to limit food production or prevent farm income from rising. In looking at the system as a whole, tension points can usually be identified and agricultural policies geared to relieving them.

This is quite different from recommending a general policy of trying to improve everything about the farm, which would be expensive and slow. Yet, in low-income countries, this latter is the normal strategy for development of the peasant economy and food production. Agricultural programs in most countries read like a standard restaurant menu: new crop varieties, improved seed, better credit, and so on. All such policies are in theory good, but each peasant farming type has its own distinctive problems or tension points, and it is best to discover these and employ the appropriate remedies. As an example, in one very steeply sloping peasant farming area in the Caribbean, soil erosion is a serious menace, but soil conservation efforts by government have been rather unsuccessful. The main goal of soil conservation is to persuade farmers to employ tree crops, which are erosion-preventers, instead of ground crops, which make the situation worse. On inspection, one finds that the major reason farmers fail to plant tree crops on steep land is that they do not own the land: farmers in this culture, because of a long history of instability in tenure, will never plant trees on rented land, since they do not expect to reap the benefits of their labor. Therefore, soil erosion in this context is a matter of land reform; land tenure is the tension point.

Here is another example: In one rather sparsely populated area of South America, the prevailing farming system is a variety of peasant agriculture called shifting or "slash-and-burn" cultivation, in which farmers set fire to a piece of forest land and plant it; then, the next year, move to another piece which they burn and plant, continuing this procedure for a number of years before returning to the first piece. This is a very long-term rotation, and obviously each farm family needs a great deal of land to pursue this system. Efforts to persuade the farmers to give up their shifting system and adopt a more intensive system of permanent cultivation on one piece of land have been unsuccessful. The reason was thought to be farmers' ignorance of the benefits of intensive cultivation. But a close look at the system showed the limiting factor to be this: permanent agriculture on that particular soil and topography would have required a considerable cash investment; if the aim were to produce ground crops, heavy fertilizer dressings would have been needed; if the aim were to produce tree crops, farmers would have needed cash to sustain them through the years before the trees began bearing. So the system did not change. But nearby, in an area where urban development has provided a good food market and has raised the cost of farm labor, the system is actually stabilizing itself. Here the market provides farmers with the necessary capital to abandon shifting agriculture, and they are doing so.

In general, then, it can be said that policies designed to improve either the income or the production of peasant farms depend, in part, on a study of the land-use system as a whole and a diagnosis of its limiting factors or tension points. The system is geographic. The diagnostician is the geographer.

SUGGESTED READINGS

Belshaw, C. S., *Traditional Exchange and Modern Markets.* Englewood Cliffs, N.J.: Prentice-Hall, Inc., 1965.

Blaut, J. M., "The Ecology of Tropical Farming Systems." In *Planta-*

tion Systems of the New World. Washington, D.C.: Pan American Union, 1959.

Franklin, S. H., "Reflections on the Peasantry." *Pacific Viewpoint,* III (1962), 1–26.

Mellor, J. W., *The Economics of Agricultural Development.* Ithaca, N.Y.: Cornell University Press, 1966.

Mukherjee, P. K., *Economic Surveys in Underdeveloped Countries.* New York: Asia Publishing House, 1959.

Pelzer, K. J., *Pioneer Settlement in the Asiatic Tropics; Studies in Land Utilization and Agricultural Colonization in Southeastern Asia.* New York: American Geographical Society, 1945.

Schultz, T. W., *Transforming Traditional Agriculture,* New Haven, Conn.: Yale University Press, 1964.

Wolf, E., *Peasants.* Englewood Cliffs, N.J.: Prentice-Hall, Inc., 1966.

15 GEOGRAPHIC ASPECTS OF PLANNING FOR NEW RURAL SETTLING IN THE FREE WORLD'S NORTHERN LANDS

Kirk H. Stone

From the times of ancient geography until the present, the study of the form of rural settlement and the process of rural settling has been an important part of the discipline. A great heritage of analyses was established by nineteenth-century geographers, such as von Richthofen and Hettner, as well as by members of sister disciplines such as the surveyor-historian Meitzen and the forester Gradmann. This was enriched through international studies, particularly in the morphological aspects, by early twentieth-century geographers, such as Schluter, Kotzschke, Demangeon, Lefevre, Grano, and Bowman. However, after the depression of the mid-1930's, internationally comparative work lagged. Only recently has it been revived by a few such geographers as Schwarz, Czacka, Houston, and Mendöl.

Yet the need for continuation of rural settling studies is greater than ever. Settlements are becoming more numerous and more complex in form. Some new rural settling and resettling activities are taking place. But the world's lands which are geographically and physically best are already largely occupied; they were noted so by Bowman, more than thirty years ago. So complete inventories and carefully laid plans are sorely needed to insure the permanence of a new rural settlement as well as the efficient employment of the people, time, and money used in the process of settling. This means that every possibility for the transfer of experiences in rural settling should be explored.

One such possibility is in the Free World's higher latitudes. In northern North America, here called Nornam, is and will be some new rural settling. But recent experience in Nørnam is limited. On the other hand, in the Scandinavian states and Finland, called Norden, settlement is centuries old; and areal advance and retreat not only have been going on there for many decades but are continuing. Because of the geographical similarities of Nornam and Norden (and, of course, allowing for the differences) a comparative study of rural settling processes in both was begun in 1950. The long-range objective was to learn how Nordenic experiences might be used in planning for new rural settling in Nornam. Preliminary guides of different types have been determined, and now it is certain that they can be refined and additional guides outlined.

However, both Nornam and Norden are large as well as physically and culturally diverse. Both to determine the guides and to apply them require the subdivision of such areas into comparable zones. These are most significantly delineated in the Northern Lands, and perhaps throughout the world, on the bases of small-scale and large-scale considerations of the isolation of the settlers.

GEOGRAPHIC MEASURES OF ISOLATION

The more isolated that people are the more dependent are neighbors on each other. Thus, the first measure of isolation made here is of the availability of settlers for emergency or short-time aid to each other. It is assumed that people are available for such if they are no more than three miles apart; that is, if the maximum time for travel on foot between two homes is one hour and the average speed is three miles per hour. The actual measure is of the number of major directions in which neighbors are less than three miles from any one family. When these are determined by mapping the locations of inhabited dwellings, there are four principal patterns of distribution of people which designate significant degrees of isolation. (Note, in Table 15–1, the terminology in the population distribution column.) They are (and the number of major directions to neighbors less than three miles from any one settler): interrupted areas and clusters of groups (many near neighbors in at least six major directions), groups of clusters and short and long lines (near neighbors mostly in three to six directions), clusters of spots and occasional short lines (one to three directions), and spots (none to one). In other words, the less areal and the more spotty the distribution of residences the less likely a settler can get emergency or short-time aid.

The second measure is of the location of the residences with respect to existing transport routes. This may supplement or extend the first measure but its major importance is as an index of the possible movement into an area of people and materials for new settling as well as the movement outward of settlers and their products. The index is the number of major directions a settler can go, within ten to twenty miles of his house, on a kind of transport route (Table 15–1). It is measured individually for railroads, roads, water routes, and air routes. Each of the four is divided into interregional and local types with the former being generally an all-weather, bulk transport line on which direct and extraregional service is provided regularly and often, while local routes are classed as those suitable for bulk transport only seasonally.

It is by the mapping of combinations of these two measures, disclosing degrees of regional and local isolation of settlers, that settlement regions and fringe of settlement zones are delineated. In the high latitudes there is a general poleward progression of the

TABLE 15–1. *Measures of Isolation in a Fringe-of-Settlement Region.*

MEASURES OF ISOLATION

REGION, ZONE, TYPE	POPULATION DISTRIBUTION PATTERN	RAIL-ROAD		ROAD		WATER		AIR		SYNTHESIS: RELATIVE DEGREE OF ISOLATION	
		INTER-REGIONAL	LOCAL	INTER-REGIONAL	LOCAL	INTER-REGIONAL	LOCAL	INTER-REGIONAL	LOCAL	REGIONAL	LOCAL
POLEWARD ↑											
UNPOPULATED	None (No population)									Very High	Very High
DISCONTINUOUS SETTLEMENT											
4. Outermost Fringe Zone											
Inland Type	Spots	0	0	0	0	0	0-1s	0	0	Very High	High
3. Outer Fringe Zone											
Inland Type	Clusters of Spots, Occasional	0	0	0	1-2	0	0-1s	0	0-1		Moderate
Coastal Type	Short Lines	0	0	0	1-2s	0-1	1-3	0	0-1s		
2. Middle Fringe Zone											
Inland Type	Groups of Clusters, Short and	0-1	1-2	0-1	2-3	0	0-1s	0-1	0-1	Moderate-Low	Low-Moderate
Coastal Type	Long Lines	0-1	0-1	0-1	1-3	1-3	1-4	0-3	0		
1. Inner Fringe Zone											
Inland Type	Interrupted Areas, Clusters of	0-2	0-2	0-2	3-4	0	0-3s	0-1	0-1	Low	Low
Coastal Type	Groups	0-2	0-3	0-2	3-4	1s	1-4s	0-3	0-1		
CONTINUOUS SETTLEMENT	Uninterrupted Areas	1-2	2-4	1-3	3-4	0-3	0-4	0-3	0-4	Very Low	None

NUMBER OF ROUTES PROVIDING ACCESS*

* —Within approximately 10–20 English miles of each permanent resident.

s —Only summer access on some or all routes.

regions from one of Continuous Settlement, to Discontinuous Settlement, to Unpopulated. In greater detail, and within just the Discontinuous Settlement regions, are usually four zones, representing degrees of isolation in terms of difficulty for new settling (Table 15–1). The range is from fewest problems for a new settler in the Inner Fringe Zone, to more in the Middle Fringe, to prohibitive and increasing numbers in the Outer and Outermost Fringe Zones. But, it is also from the geographical characteristics of these zones in Norden, and the study of rural settling elsewhere in the world, that preliminary guides for new rural settling in Nornam can be determined.

NORDENIC FRINGE OF SETTLEMENT ZONES

The measures of isolation were developed empirically in Norden. Applied there they disclose the presence of three regions: (1) one of Continuous Settlement, including all of Denmark and southern parts of Norway, Sweden, and Finland, (2) a small Unpopulated Region in central Iceland, and (3) a large Discontinuous Settlement region in the rest of Norden, comprising more than three-quarters of its area (Figure 15–1). The southern edge of the Discontinuous Settlement Region is a narrow belt extending from south of Iceland to about 62°N. in eastern Finland; generally northwestward from it are the four fringe settlement zones, the Inner and Middle Fringe Zones in belts and the other two in interrupted belt-like areas.

More specifically, the Inner Fringe Zone has three parts. The western Norwegian averages about 30 miles (48 km.) wide, and the Swedish and Finnish sections about 75 miles (120 km.). Residences are usually grouped in interrupted areas of closely spaced individual homes. Each part has interregional transport of one or two railroads, two to five roads, one or two air routes, and a water route. Local access is by railroads a maximum of 35 to 50 miles

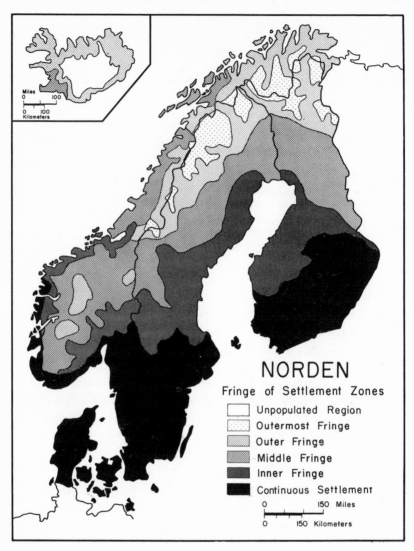

NORDEN

Fringe of Settlement Zones

- Unpopulated Region
- Outermost Fringe
- Outer Fringe
- Middle Fringe
- Inner Fringe
- Continuous Settlement

0   150 Miles

0   150 Kilometers

Figure 15–1

(56 to 80 km.) apart, roads going in three or four directions within about 15 miles (24 km.) of every settler, and several kinds of water transport. The exception is the western Norwegian coast where interregional and local water traffic are substitutes for other kinds of transportation.

The Middle Fringe Zone is U-shaped, 40 to 110 miles (64 to 177 km.) wide and broken into four sections. Dwellings are in groups of clusters and occasional long lines excepting two interrupted areas in the Icelandic part. Perhaps half of the zone's area is uninhabited, most of that being in linear patches up to 9 to 12 miles (14 to 19 km.) wide. Some settlers in the mainland part are within about 20 miles (32 km.) of one interregional railroad, road, or air route while the Icelandic part has at least three interregional routes by both sea and air. Other people depend on local routes: some are near a railroad (except, of course, in Iceland), most are close to two or three roads and a seasonal water route, and those in the coastal Middle Fringes of Norway and Iceland have all-year boat service. In the Swedish and Finnish parts of the zone there have been major recent changes in patterns of settlement as a result of abandonment and new settling, respectively.

The Outer Fringe Zone comprises the remaining Icelandic coast, three small southern Norwegian areas, and an interrupted strip, 50 to 150 miles (80 to 240 km.) wide, from the middle Norwegian-Swedish border to the northern Finnish-Soviet boundary. Throughout this section the residences are in clusters of spots, some short lines, and individual spots, so much of the zone is uninhabited and many have a high degree of isolation. Interregional transport, for example, is lacking except in north Norway where there is a water route. For local traffic there are several routes for ships along the Icelandic and Norwegian coasts, and elsewhere roads (some seasonal) go in one or two directions near only some of the settlers. Air service is very limited.

In general, then, the areas where useful Nordenic settling experiences are to be found are large and varied. They are the

227

Inner and Middle Fringe Zones, both coastal and inland types, extending from southwestern Norway to northern Sweden and Finland (Figure 15–1). They include occupational combinations of fishing, forestry, agriculture, and industry and represent zones whose boundaries are partly advancing, while others are stable, and still others are retreating.

NORNAMIC FRINGE OF SETTLEMENT ZONES

In Nornam the same regions and zones are present. However, their spatial relationships are more complex than in Norden. The Continuous Settlement region is composed of two parts. The western one is from 100 to 200 miles (160 to 320 km.) wide and centered on a line from central Saskatchewan southeastward about 500 miles (800 km.) to central-southern Manitoba (Figure 15–2). The eastern one is from 50 to 125 miles (80 to 200 km.) wide and centered on a line from Windsor, Ontario, northeastward more than 700 miles (1125 km.) to Quebec City. In both, there are practically no interruptions in tracts of at least a few hundred square miles and most of the land is used for agriculture. Eastward, to the north, and westward of them is a great Discontinuous Settlement Region, varying in width from about 320 to 900 miles (515 to 1450 km.) and extending from eastern Newfoundland to western Alaska. The remainder of Nornam is the Unpopulated Region, in five major parts from central Labrador to northern Alaska. Each section is hundreds of miles in dimension and without transport routes and permanent residents excepting at some specialized sites for military and weather observations.

If examined more closely, the Discontinuous Settlement Region also has the same four fringe of settlement zones found in Norden.

The Inner Fringe Zone is limited to four southerly locations in

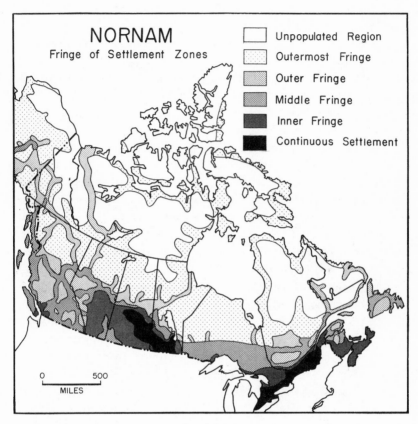

Figure 15–2

Canada. Two small areas are in southwestern British Columbia and on the northwestern Lake Superior shore; the former is mapped provisionally until the adjacent United States has been classified. The Inner Fringe of the Prairie Provinces has three arms, of which the two westernmost are 100 to 150 miles (160 to 240 km.) wide and separated by 200 miles (320 km.). The two extend north of the border nearly 400 miles (640 km.) to beyond Edmonton and are mapped as Inner Fringe because of interruptions in continuity of population closeness in the vicinity of Battleford, Saskatchewan, and in southern Alberta; a third and northern arm is narrow, 15 to 60 miles (24 to 96 km.) wide, and runs from about Prince Albert to southeastern Manitoba. Farther eastward, to the east of Lake Huron, the Inner Fringe is wider, about 150 miles (240 km.), but it narrows in southern Quebec before widening again in the Maritime Provinces where, again, final mapping awaits classification of the adjacent United States.

The Middle Fringe Zone has seven occurrences, commonly linear in shape (Figure 15-2). On the west is the Alaska Railroad Belt, between the south coastal ports of Seward and Anchorage and the inland city of Fairbanks, a strip about 420 miles (675 km.) long. Eastward, in southeastern Alaska, is another area; there population is in groups of clusters and coastal ferry transport and air service substitute for some of the lack of interregional railroad and road transport. South of the Prince Rupert and Peace River railroads are several linear patches on the coast and inland; on eastward the zone pinches out near Prince Albert but reoccurs as a small area in western Manitoba. The largest part of the Middle Fringe is across central Ontario where a belt is 100 to 200 miles (160 to 320 km.) wide but this splits into two narrow ones around an island of Outer Fringe Zone in southwestern Quebec, and then separates into one strip on the north shore of the lower St. Lawrence and another in the northern Maritime Provinces and central Newfoundland; in the last two, water transport is a common substitute for railroads and occasionally for roads.

The outer Fringe Zone of Nornam often is linear, also. This is because many parts are composed of short lines of population and the end sections of roads. The zone's parts are widespread, ranging from South Central Alaska and the Western Canadian mountains eastward to two parts of Newfoundland and the southern Labrador coast. The four extensions northward are the railroads, substitutes for access by local roads, to central Labrador and Hudson Bay ports and the road-air-seasonal-water route from the Peace River area to the Mackenzie River's mouth. Quite notable is the complete absence of the zone in central Alberta and in central Ontario where population and transport patterns change so abruptly that the Outer Fringe is skipped.

The Outermost Fringe Zone, most isolated part of the region, has a spotty population distribution of small villages 25 to 100 miles (40 to 150 km.) apart and transport is limited to seasonal water or widely separated and seasonal air routes. The zone is nearly continuous from Alaska (where it is more than half of the state's area) in two directions: the first extends eastward in a narrow coastal belt to Middle Labrador, while the second goes southeastward in a 200 to 500 mile-wide (320 to 800 km.) belt almost to the St. Lawrence River. The farmer has exceptionally good communication and transport facilities at the Distant Early Warning stations, but these are specialized installations and the dismantling of some already has started.

Additional research in Nornam is necessary before this provisional mapping may be verified. Nevertheless, the mapping discloses zones similar to those in Norden. Study of their similarities and differences, and preliminary testing of the measures of isolation elsewhere in the Free World reveal twelve general guides which might be useful when planning for new rural settling in Nornam.

GENERAL RURAL SETTLING GUIDES

First is that new settling at the edges of the inhabited world is a natural and continuing action. It should not be considered exceptional. Present throughout history have been the attractions to nations of political, economic, or military advantages and to individuals of cheap land, potential increase of income, or greater freedom. Meanwhile, in the highly developed regions there have been the repelling forces of dense population, rigorous competition, and some economic maladjustment. In addition, new settling usually has been encouraged by nations at their fringes—by their either sponsoring it directly or simply permitting it to take place. All these forces probably will continue. Yet, continuance of new rural settling should be by selective processes determined from frequent analyses of what is happening throughout the world.

Second, if new rural settling is to be encouraged in Nornam it might best be limited geographically. Initial efforts could be directed to the proved parts of the Continuous Settlement region. Then, within the region of Discontinuous Settlement, success is more likely if efforts are limited to individual or group settling in the better parts of the Inner Fringe Zone and secondarily, to only group settling in the best localities of the Middle Fringe Zone. The freedom to settle anywhere at all is an expense that few, if any, governments can afford to permit either now or in the future. One may learn from Sweden that it is easy to overextend settling in the Middle Fringe Zone and even in the Inner Fringe —in parts of both the abandonment of agricultural-forestry units is now a major problem. Also, it is highly probable that in the Outer and Outermost Fringe Zones new settling should be severely restricted, if permitted at all. In them only highly specialized uses of selected points, rather than areas, should be considered, and these as a part of a multifunctional and long-term plan for nonmilitary activities.

Third, a degree of detailed locational planning little used as yet in Nornam probably is advisable. Simply permitting or encouraging settlement and providing some public services probably is not enough. To reduce the overall costs of development is likely to require planning on the order of that in the Dutch polders where the locations of rural bus stops, individual farmsteads, specific buildings, types of villages, and certain service establishments are determined before construction starts. To be sure, this introduces an aspect of regimentation. However, all opportunities are usually accompanied by responsibilities; and the complexities of new rural settling in the twentieth century on less than the best land should be done with national and local community financial resources and requirements in mind as well as the permanence of the settlers.

Fourth, the selection of settlers should be considered the most important element of the process. Further, selection probably should be only in terms of an area to which people are going, not in terms of the relief of a problem in the locality from which they come. And, it must be recognized that there is still great need in the world for determining how to select settlers. Certainly, judgments of reliability (as of the Japanese in Latin America), of necessary experience (as in Finland), of financial capability (as in the Netherlands), and of the many other personal and professional qualities needed (as in Australia and Israel) should be as carefully measured as are the blood strains in a herd of cattle, the annual production of a forest, the design of a house, and the spacing and size of drainage tile. The "human engineering" must exceed the civil and agricultural engineering. After all, settling is by and for the settlers.

Fifth, new settling might be best if just by short-distance movements. Actually, it is likely that new settling will be based upon movements of people for distances of only 50 to 200 miles (80 to

320 km.). It may be anticipated that the few present long-distance-immigrant areas of Canada, South America, Israel, and Australia are likely to have little or no new rural settling by such immigration in another ten years. Steps already taken in some of these countries and the experiences of primarily local movement in Norden show that in planning for Nornam's future it will be wise to be conservative geographically. By short-distance moves, the settlers will know their areas' physical and cultural conditions and the adjustments will be minimal. However, if there are to be long-distance movements they should take more time than previously and allow for training periods in the new area such as those used in Israel.

Sixth, the economy of a new settler probably ought to be based upon at least two occupations. This is partly so there will be a cash income in the first years of settling. More important, it is an adjustment to the use of more than one resource in an area where any one occupation may not be sufficient to support a settler's family totally or every year. Even in the region of Continuous Settlement in Norden, one finds numerous bi-occupational people, such as farmer-foresters and farmer-fishermen, and there appears little reason to assume that new Nornamic settlement (or that anywhere else) should be based on a single occupation. For decades, one characterization of a "pioneer" has been that he or she did many things for himself. With more tools and more extensive communications now, it is easier to be multi-occupational. Further, the isolation of the Discontinuous Settlement Region often is a stimulant to variety in self-help.

Seventh, each specific area of new settling would profit from having one or more exemplary settlers. These could be carefully selected people who are to be living examples of what national and local officials may say should be done. This has been used in several places in the world (especially in at least one north Norwegian locality), and their effectiveness is often greater if they are not government employees or if their activities are not supplemented by governmental equipment or financing.

Eighth, inventories of physical and cultural conditions and needs probably should be completed at least three years prior to first settling. This is essential if the data are to be used in the planning for the action. Further, physical and economic adjustments take time. If careful inventories are made early and used properly some possible accomplishments might be: swamps turned into productive land economically, types of forests allocated so new settlers could have cash incomes in the early years, people already in an area of proposed new settling could be assimilated harmoniously, and there could be time for efficient construction of public utilities and provision of basic services.

Ninth, there probably should be quite detailed timing of general and individual settling activities. In the past, the overall phases of the development of an area have been charted and often correctly. However, most contemporary new settling starts in a commercialized world where temporal organization is essential—products must be ready for scheduled transport, and for a particular market at a certain time. Further, the timing of such details as the movement of the members of each new settler's family to a new agricultural site requires study and careful action. In some parts of Norway and Finland, it has been thought best for the farmer to spend most of the first year on the new place alone. In others, the whole family moved at the beginning and shared all the problems and inconveniences of starting everything at once. In Finland, for example, a family of six to ten people living for the first winter in a 10-by-12-foot which is to be the sauna certainly contributes to "togetherness"—but also to problems. It is doubtful that all the alternatives of detailed timing are known, much less the answers, but experiences in Norden and elsewhere make it clear that settlers no longer can just guess how to do it.

Tenth, the settlers' initial investments of time and money need be quite carefully managed. Unqualified giving of materials, aid, or credit has to be controlled skillfully and probably on an individual basis. However it is done, the settlers ought to be maneuvered so as to feel the investments are reasonable in amount,

235

effective economically, and—most of all—theirs from the beginning. Experimentation with and study of how this phase of new settling has been handled elsewhere are high-priority needs at present.

Eleventh, where new Nornamic settling is to be agricultural, a fresh view of farm size and the contiguity of parcels may be useful. Farms there might be 500 to 600 acres large and made up of several separate parcels. Persons with sentimental feelings for American homesteading acts and their limits of 160 and 320 acres will be dismayed by this—but so would Nordenic, Israeli, and some Dutch farmers whose area is based on the quality of the land and the amount of that quality which is necessary to support a family. Further, although it may seem geographically sacrilegious to suggest that a farm in Nornam be composed of five or more different parcels, the experiences of thousands of Finns have shown that such parcelization is one way of effectively evening out the random distributions of varying-quality forests, swamps, and moraines.

Twelfth, an area of new settlement should be expected to take at least twenty to thirty years to begin to mature sociologically, psychologically, politically, and economically. This means that few governments can or should consider a colonization effort as a politically advantageous move (unless, of course, they can guarantee such longevity). The first three years in a new settling effort are the most critical to the individual settler; after one is through this starting period he faces a longer second phase of refinement of occupations, consolidation of gains, and development of regular growth. During the latter phase, a settler may be able to look beyond immediate requirements and contribute to community life. And, of course, major progress toward permanence of settlement is made when the children of the original settlers take over, especially when they develop the area further and participate in its government. But all of this takes time. The process of settling should be considered as a long-term investment

—first in the settlers, and second in the area involved. Permanence can hardly be gained by speed—people take time to grow in an area just as other organisms do.

These twelve general guides are the results of initial considerations of Norden and Nornam, as mapped by the suggested measures of isolation in combination with study of rural settling elsewhere. Other general guides are considered minor, only partially transferable, or incomplete. But additions may be expected, all to be added to the existing suggestions of Sir Bernard O. Binns, Professor A. Maughini, and specialists working for or with the Intergovernmental Committee for European Migration. Still, all too little effort is being spent on the contemporary process of new rural settling in all parts of the world.

In retrospect, it may seem that there has been little progress in developing the "science of settlement" Bowman suggested as necessary in 1926. However, we do know that any settling in the mid-twentieth century is complex, made more so in specific areas by national desires and international and national trends. And these are dynamic. So we recognize that a universal set of rules for settling probably is unattainable. Still, comparative geographic study discloses clear signs of repeating patterns in the process of new rural settling in the Free World's northern lands, and its other areas as well. With this encouragement and with the realization that new rural settling is a natural and continuing force, we can but continue the search for guides because help is so sorely needed in this phase of initiating permanent man-land relationships.

SUGGESTED READINGS

Binns, B. O., *Land Settlement for Agriculture*, FAO Development Paper No. 9. Rome, Italy: FAO, 1951.

Bowman, I., "The Scientific Study of Settlement." *Geographical Review*, XVI (1926), 647–653.

International Committee for European Migration, *Report of the Director on Land Settlement*. Geneva, Switz.: mimeographed, August 30, 1956.

Maughini, Armando, *General Remarks on Land Settlement in Overseas Countries*. Geneva, Switz.: International Committee for European Migration; mimeographed, 1953.

Mendöl, T., *Általános Településföldrajz*. Budapest: Akadémiai Kiadó, 1963.

Schwarz, G., *Allgemeine Siedlungsgeographie*. Berlin: De Gruyter, 1966.

Stone, K. H., "Swedish Fringes of Settlement." *Annals of the Association of American Geographers*, LII (1962), 373–393.

Stone, K. H., "The Development of a Focus for the Geography of Settlement." *Economic Geography*, XVI (1965), 346–355.

Stone, K. H., "Geographical Characteristics of Alaskan Fringes of Settlement." *Papers of the Alaskan Science Conference*, Juneau, Alaska, 1965.

16 MAN'S NEW VIEWS OF THE EARTH: THE POTENTIAL OF REMOTE SENSING

Robert H. Alexander

The old saying "You can't see the forest for the trees" illustrates the fact that it is often necessary to get away from what we are looking at in order to really see it. A geographer standing in the middle of a forest may have an excellent view of fifteen or twenty tree trunks, but no idea of how large the forest is or where he is in relation to nearby mountains or rivers, or how to find his way out of the forest to the nearest road or city.

A more geographic way of stating the forest and trees problem is that it is important to be able to view our environment from various distances and vantage points; for some purposes we want to concentrate our attention on a single tree close at hand, while for other purposes we want to take in a whole assemblage of trees in a single view. It is useful, then, for the geographer to get up above the forest, to obtain the "mountain view."

Remote sensing can be described as the process of obtaining the "mountain view"—the process of obtaining data about the earth's surface by means of cameras or other devices which can look down on that surface from above. The product of remote sensing which is most familiar is the aerial photograph, a well-established tool for geographers. Photographs taken from different altitudes, or with different types of cameras, can give us a bird's-eye view of our surroundings at a variety of scales. An aerial photograph which has a scale of 1:10,000, for example, compresses a distance of 100 meters on the ground to one centimeter on the photograph, and such a photograph would be extremely helpful to the geographer who wants to see what his forest looks like.

Recent gains in technology, however, promise that geography can move even beyond the limits of the mountaintop view and the aerial photograph. With the availability of new kinds of vehicles to carry the sensors aloft, such as sounding rockets and earth-orbiting spacecraft, and with the development of sensors which reach far beyond the visible portion of the spectrum recorded in a conventional aerial photograph, geography is now facing the possibility of getting data on a world-wide basis never dreamed of before. In exploring this new possibility we shall first try to place remote sensing in its proper perspective as one of many tools the geographer can use in his task of studying the earth's surface as the environment of man. Advantages of remote sensing over more conventional ground-based tools will be noted. Then we shall look at some of the sensors themselves and what they can do. Finally, we shall explore the exciting promise of a geographic remote sensing system which might be placed in orbit around the earth, providing a continuing supply of the data we need to understand our environment and to help solve the practical problems of sustaining our life on this planet.

The basic purpose of using remote sensing in geography is to provide detailed, and, if desired, permanent records of phenomena of geographic interest, which include the whole domain of man at and near the surface of the earth—the configuration of the land and of water bodies, the moving waters and winds and the changes they bring about on the land surface, the plant and animal life that covers the earth, the climatic factors, and particularly the works of man.

This domain is continuously bathed in electromagnetic energy coming in a great variety of wavelengths spread out over a broad spectrum. Most of this energy is supplied either directly or indirectly by the sun. Wavelengths may be extremely short like those of the X-rays, no longer than the ten-millionth part of a millimeter; or they may be extremely long like radio waves with lengths of meters or even kilometers. Intermediate between these extremes is the visible light spectrum, with wavelengths ranging from violet at about four tenths of a micron to red at about seven tenths of a micron (a micron being the thousandth part of a millimeter).

A number of things can happen to the energy upon its arrival from the sun. It might be scattered and diffused in the atmosphere. It might penetrate through the atmosphere to the earth's surface and be reflected directly back into the atmosphere and space. Energy arriving as visible light may be absorbed by land, water, and vegetation surfaces, and then be re-emitted as longer wavelength infrared (heat) radiation, providing while doing so the driving force for such vital processes as evaporation and photosynthesis.

Surfaces vary widely in their reflection, absorption, and re-emission of energy and it is this variation that gives materials their characteristic colors and textural appearances. Recent studies indicate that in many cases these characteristics might be so distinctive that careful measurements of the wavelength (color) of the reflected and emitted energy from many natural substances might be used for remote identification of those substances. Different species of vegetation, for example, have characteristic differences in the intensity and wavelength of the reflected light, not only in the greens which our eyes see, but also in the wavelengths which are just too long to be seen, those in the part of the spectrum called the near-infrared. These facts suggest that we might build up a key or catalog showing the characteristics of reflected light for different species of plants, and by this means use the photographs or other images obtained by remote sensing to identify and make maps of plant distribution, whether natural plant communities or agricultural crops. What is true with plants is true to some extent with other phenomena of geographic interest, such as soils, rock outcrops, road surfaces, building materials, or possibly commodities being shipped by rail, truck, or barge. The information about these phenomena that could be made available would be of immense value to geographers, who heretofore have had to obtain it by means of laborious and costly ground studies.

Thus remote sensing extends horizons—in space, in time, and in the electromagnetic spectrum. It extends horizons in space by both stretching the line of sight and compressing the field of view, allowing a smaller scale, larger area observation which may give the geographer at once a regional integration which formerly took days, weeks, or months to build up from isolated surface observations. It extends horizons in time by speeding up data collection—allowing rapid coverage, and enabling regional data gathering and mapping to be done much faster than by conventional ground procedures. Finally, remote sensing extends horizons in the electromagnetic spectrum, enabling us not only to select diagnostic wavelengths of visible light, but also to obtain valuable environmental information as revealed by the energy reflected and emitted in the nonvisible ultraviolet, infrared, microwave, and radio bands of the spectrum.

The extending of horizons is one of the first steps in a series of geographic processes that begins with observations at a particular site or locality, and leads to the development of generalizations about that locality's relationships with neighboring areas. Such generalizations can be made without remote sensing—the ability to produce small-scale maps has been precisely this ability to extend our view beyond the horizon. But with remote sensing, the data-gathering and data-integration tasks are enormously simplified, and we are much more easily able to incorporate larger and larger sections of the earth's surface into our field of observation, and to see comparisons of distant areas with those close at hand so that a generalized overview of portions of the earth's surface—and eventually of the whole earth—can be presented. The growth of geographic science has always depended upon an increasing ability to generalize from regional comparisons: first in terms of area, by extending the visible horizon; and then in conceptual terms, by means of maps, equations, and other abstracted representations of geographic phenomena.

Much research still has to be done before we will know just how much of our needed information can be supplied by remote sensors. But it seems clear that geographers who are interested in obtaining data about the features on the earth's surface will find it to their advantage to learn something about the physics and chemistry of remote sensing in order to take advantage of the newer methods for obtaining data. Once we learn the chemical and physical characteristics of the surface of the objects about which we want to obtain data, it is then simply a matter of selecting the proper sensors and recording devices that will be sensitive to radiation in those wavelengths. For those wavelengths that are visible to our naked eye, ordinary cameras with special selections of films and filters will do the job. Furthermore, these cameras can respond to wavelengths beyond the visible into the photographic infrared and will thus give us more information than we could see by looking at the same phenomena.

Some parts of the spectrum have been much less explored and are not even accessible to photographic film. Ultraviolet light, with wavelengths shorter than those of visible light, is apparently useful for distinguishing between mineral substances of different composition. The longer-than-visible wavelengths of the infrared and microwave bands carry important information about our thermal environment. We need special kinds of sensors to obtain information in these wavelengths, and special kinds of devices to transfer the information into a form that will be visible to our eyes.

The portion of the infrared spectrum between wavelengths of

about four microns and fourteen microns is particularly interesting to us because it contains two of the "windows" through which our atmosphere is transparent. These "windows" are the bands between 4.5 and 5.5 microns, and between 8 and 14 microns. So a sensor high above the earth's surface would respond to radiation emitted from the surface within these bands. One device which will sense this radiation is a scanning radiometer in which the sensor sweeps rapidly over the field of view and records the intensity of radiation at each spot much the same way that a television scanner scans a picture in the visible part of the spectrum and reconstructs it electronically somewhere else.

The scanned image can be reconstructed on photographic film so that it looks very much like a photograph, with bright spots representing warm areas and dark spots representing cool areas. Such an image represents a kind of temperature map, and its utility in the study of the geography of weather and climate is obvious.

The newer sensing and scanning techniques are also applicable in the microwave portion of the spectrum, where wavelengths range from slightly less than a millimeter to twenty or thirty centimeters. Microwaves of certain wavelengths can penetrate several centimeters or even meters of soil, water, snow, and ice, thereby promising valuable information on soil moisture profiles, depth of snow or ice, and possibly temperature profiles in soil and water. These techniques have many applications in agricultural and water resource studies.

The camera and radiometer sensing systems mentioned so far can be described as passive systems; that is, the sensors merely respond to reflected or emitted radiation which is already there. On the other hand, there are active sensing systems—for example, night photography with flash bulbs and radar—in which the radiation is supplied artificially at the time the sensing is accomplished. Radar sensing employs radiation with wavelengths ranging from about one centimeter to one meter. When used for geographic purposes, the airplane or other vehicle on which the radar is mounted carries an energy source which illuminates the landscape, if the word "illuminate" can be used when talking about radiation in spectral bands which are invisible to our eyes. This radiation is then reflected from the surface back to the sensor and reconstituted electronically into an image which can be displayed on a cathode ray tube or printed on photographic film. The resulting image can be made to have photographic quality although the longer the wavelengths of the radiation the poorer the resolution capability of the sensors; radar sensors can never have as fine a resolution as cameras. Radar sensing, however, is adequate for many geographic purposes, and has the capability of penetrating clouds and of operating both day and night. Radar images could therefore be used for such tasks as terrain mapping in the tropics, or Arctic and Antarctic ice surveys, regardless of weather or season.

A more recent development in active remote sensing systems involves the use of lasers—high-intensity monochromatic light beams which can be used to obtain very accurate altitude profiles by careful timing of the reflections from surface features.

Thus far we have been discussing the sensors themselves and the kinds of data they can collect. These are developments which have already taken place; that is, the sensors described here have already been built and have been used in varying degrees to obtain geographic data.

The really exciting promise in remote sensing is yet to come— the possibility of placing sensors aboard earth-orbiting spacecraft to complete the exploration of the earth and then to update our knowledge of changes in the earth's geography continually. Systems of earth-viewing sensors in orbiting spacecraft could obtain the first uniform, world-wide, systematic environmental surveys of the surface of our planet.

Even though a geographic satellite system has yet to be built, we can foresee a number of advantages in such a system. The

245

whole earth could be covered fast enough to provide an almost synoptic view of the planet. What changes are taking place simultaneously on opposite sides of the globe? Where are all the ocean-going ships at any given time? With a geographic satellite system we could come closer than ever before to answers for questions such as these.

The orbiting remote sensors would make it possible to view the earth at a variety of scales. Spacecraft observations would be especially valuable for obtaining small-scale coverage which would provide a single view of large portions of the earth's surface. But by using more powerful lenses on the cameras, for example, even quite large-scale views of small areas could be obtained. Roads, houses, and even automobiles should be within the resolution capabilities of spaceborne remote sensor systems.

A whole battery of sensors embracing a large part of the electromagnetic spectrum could be placed aboard a single orbiting remote sensing laboratory. Thus the advantages of each wavelength could be utilized, as dictated by time of day and geographical and meteorological conditions. There is no single wavelength which will fulfill geographic data requirements; the strength of the sensing system lies in its combination of all useful sensors.

Finally, surprising as it may seem, the spacecraft remote sensing systems may actually prove to be more economical than either airborne systems or networks of ground observations. The enormous costs of launching and supporting spacecraft may be offset by efficiencies in combining the data needs of many users, and by the ease with which the remote, isolated, and antipodal regions can be reached.

Besides being of inestimable value to basic geographic science with its goal of understanding the man-environment system on the earth's surface, remote sensing surveys from spacecraft would have many immediate applications. Such surveys would serve the needs of inventories of agricultural, forest, and other natural resources; of basic topographic and hydrographic mapping for advanced as well as developing economies; of planning new locations for growing populations, especially in the vicinity of large urban centers, where the need is greatest at present; of energy and water balance studies which could aid in our understanding of climates; of surveillance and warning for impending natural disasters such as floods, famines, landslides; of efforts to keep tabs on the increasing menace of air and water pollution; and of a host of other environmental problems.

There should be no underestimating the difficulties in building a geographic satellite system for our planet. It is quite possible, however, that much of the technology which is already being developed would be adequate for a geographic satellite system. Most of the sensors which could be used in early earth-orbiting geographic satellites already exist; only relatively minor research and engineering tasks would be needed to fit the sensors into spacecraft.

Substantial research efforts will be needed to develop a geographic capability to utilize the data from the orbiting sensors. The field of geography would essentially have to retool to be able to make use of remote sensing data as substitutes for, and additions to, more conventional types of geographic data. As an example of preliminary research of this nature, batteries of remote sensors might be flown in airplanes over small areas which are already well known and well mapped—areas which are carefully chosen to be representative of the varieties of geographic terrain around the world. This preliminary research program could establish the utility of each of the remote sensors as geographic data-gathering tools and could assist in the selection of a combination of sensors which might be most useful in an orbiting data-gathering system. Much research is needed to figure out how to cope with the great quantities of data which could be obtained from a geographic satellite system and to develop highly sophisticated information-flow systems, incorporating automatic data processing techniques at many stages of the information systems.

But most of all what is needed is the will to go ahead and solve the problems—both technical and political—which still stand in the way of our realization of a geographic satellite system. The technical problems may be the easiest to solve. In the political realm, looking down upon the territory of sovereign nations has always been a matter of considerable delicacy. Is it too much to hope that goodwill can overcome the natural reluctance nations feel about being laid open to observation from the skies? Perhaps not. Population growth and environmental change are taking place so fast that mankind's need for data about the earth may soon outweigh his fears of opening national territories to the knowledge of all. In the space age, secrecy may have few if any of the advantages it had formerly when military intelligence had to be obtained by slow and laborious infiltration on the ground. In fact, with deterrence being one of the main theories of the maintenance of peace among the great powers, there is, to a certain extent, an inversion of the classic intelligence function of secrecy. Now a major power bloc wants a potential enemy to know that it is not bluffing and that the deterrent military power actually exists. Also, much of the job of inspection for arms control agreement could obviously be done by remote sensing from satellites. Geographers who would like to have data that a satellite system could provide can well join the ranks of those who would benefit from an international political climate which would make "open skies" a workable policy. If the whole surface of the earth is to be made available for observation by the space powers, then why not also to all the other nations as well, so that the scientists, administrators, resource managers, and all others who need geographic data for peaceful purposes can have it in time to help them solve their problems?

There will be great difficulties in building an orbiting remote sensing system for geography. But remote sensing has never been easy. Almost a century ago, William Henry Jackson brought about great advances in remote sensing with his magnificent mountaintop photographs of the Yellowstone country and other regions of the American West. Jackson endured great hardships, carrying on his back a heavy camera, large glass plates, wet chemicals, and darkroom tent to high remote vantage points. Jackson's work enlightened not only the scientific expeditions which he accompanied, by providing graphic records of the geography and geology, but also the citizens of the eastern states who were hungry for accurate knowledge of the continent into which their domain was expanding. Our difficulties might be relatively no more formidable than were Jackson's. Our geographic satellite system, like his mountaintop photographs, would have the potential of bringing enlightened understanding of our environment along with information of immense practical value to map-makers, resource developers, and all other users of information about the surface features of the planet Earth.

SUGGESTED READINGS

Bird, J. B., and Morrison, A., "Space Photography and Its Geographical Applications." *Geographical Review,* LIV, No. 4 (October 1964), 463–486.

Colwell, R. N., Brewer, W., Lauder, G., Langley, P., Morgan, J., Rinker, J., Robinson, J. M., and Soreur, A. L., "Basic Matter and Energy Relationships Involved in Remote Reconnaissance." *Photogrammetric Engineering,* XXIX (1963), 761–799.

Ewing, G. C. (ed.), *Oceanography from Space.* Woods Hole, Mass.: Woods Hole Oceanographic Institution, Ref. No. 65–10, 1965.

Ewing, G. C. (ed.), *Peaceful Uses of Earth-Observation Spacecraft.* 3 vols.; Ann Arbor, Mich.: University of Michigan, Infrared and Optical Sensor Laboratory, February 1966.

Ewing, G. C. (ed.) , *Proceedings* of the First, Second, Third, and Fourth Symposia on Remote Sensing of Environment. Ann Arbor, Mich.:

University of Michigan, Institute of Science and Technology, 1962, 1963, 1965, and 1966.

Ewing, G. C. (ed.), *Spacecraft in Geographic Research.* Report of a Conference on the Use of Orbiting Spacecraft in Geographic Research. Washington, D.C.: National Academy of Sciences—National Research Council Publication No. 1353, 1966.

17 GEOGRAPHY IN AMERICAN EDUCATION

Clyde F. Kohn

Not so long ago most Americans thought of foreign lands and peoples, if they thought of them at all, as being far away, exotic and, for the most, backward. This ignorance of Europe, Asia, Latin America, and Africa was regrettable but understandable, and of no real concern to the development of our nation. The United States during the nineteenth century had grown to strength and statehood in isolation, shielded by two large oceans, and protected by the British Navy. Moreover, the American people had before them a vast continent, rich and varied in resources, to settle and develop. There was little need for great numbers of Americans to be informed about, or interested in, the affairs of those who lived across the seas.

But times have changed, and in recent years the United States has become steadily involved in world affairs. Paradoxically, the political, technological, and social revolutions of the past few decades have not only expanded America's horizons, but they have also so narrowed our world that an astronaut can spin around it in a couple of hours. Occurrences in one part can often affect the lives of millions living in lands that were once considered remote. As a result, the education of American youth can no longer be limited to a knowledge and understanding of one's local community, state, or nation. It must now deal in depth with other national cultures and with international relations.

This growing need for all Americans to become more familiar with other lands and peoples was clearly recognized by President Johnson in an address on September 16, 1965, commemorating the two hundredth birthday of James Smithson, whose bequest led to the founding of the Smithsonian Institution. Mr. Johnson on that occasion said that he would present to Congress, in January, 1966, a five-point program, one part of which would be, "to help American schools increase their knowledge of the world and its peoples." To achieve this goal, the schools of the United States will need to provide increased opportunities for students to become better acquainted with the world in which they live, and with the role of the United States, and thus of themselves, in the emerging world community of nations. In this context, more attention will need to be given to the teaching of geography. This discipline, above all others, is concerned with studying world patterns and cultures, and with gaining insights into the many complex economic, social, and political relations that make the world a vast, highly complex system of nations and peoples.

The task for America's geography teachers will not be easy. Increased opportunities for gaining greater knowledge of the world and its peoples will need to be provided at all levels of instruction, from the kindergarten through the high schools, colleges, and universities, and for non-collegiate adults. This will require (1) the development of well-planned programs of study providing for an orderly and systematically arranged program of learning experiences, (2) the adopting of teaching techniques consistent with acceptable learning theories and practices, (3) the creation of up-to-date and varied instructional materials, and (4) the development of both pre-service and in-service educational programs to help teachers acquire the insights and techniques of instruction needed to meet the challenges of our rapidly changing role in world affairs. To assay the role of geography in American education, and to meet the challenge with which the geographical profession is confronted, attention will need to be directed to each of these four major requirements.

PROGRAMS OF STUDY IN GEOGRAPHY

In the Elementary Schools

In many of American elementary schools, geography is included in what is commonly referred to as the "social studies program." This program includes material from the various social science disciplines in a so-called fused, or integrated, approach to understanding world societies. Relatively little attention is paid to the discrete disciplines, but materials are drawn, as apparently needed, from history, geography, and the several social sciences.

Most geographers interested in the education of elementary school pupils believe they can demonstrate that geography learning suffers whenever their discipline is included in such programs of study. They strongly advocate, as a result, that geography be taught as a separate subject, at least beginning with the fourth grade. Others, although agreeing that the study of geography is often short-changed in present integrated programs of study, believe that it can be taught successfully in social studies courses, providing these are conceived as multidiscipline but coordinated programs of learning. What the outcome of the current debate will be remains uncertain at this stage. It is a fact that experts in curriculum development across the nation are giving more and more attention to the role of the separate disciplines. They feel that there should be a tailored sequential program in geography. Lip service, at least, is being paid to the need for studying certain phenomena as they are viewed by each of the individual disciplines.

Whether taught as a separate subject or in a coordinated social studies program, there has been little change in either the scope or sequence of our elementary school geography program during the past several decades. Commonly, in the primary grades, the child is made aware of his immediate area. He studies his home, school, and local community from different points of view. The concepts and methods of inquiry which he learns are representative of advanced thinking in the social science disciplines. In other words, the content offered in the primary grades in better American schools differs only in depth, not in kind, from that offered at the most advanced graduate levels. Recently, the only new trend has been the introduction of an international dimension into the geography program. For example, after primary grade children develop basic concepts and generalizations about their local community, they are given an opportunity to study local communities in other societies to see how they differ or resemble their own.

When boys and girls reach the intermediate grades, the emphasis shifts from the purely local community to the state and region in which the child lives, the United States, and to areas in and beyond the Americas. How the world is subdivided into smaller areas for study in the intermediate grades varies from place to place. The traditional way is to organize the study of the world in terms of continents. Many programs still reflect this practice with units organized around North America presented generally at the fifth-grade level, and units involving South America, Europe, Asia, Africa, and Australia for study in the sixth and seventh grades.

In recent years, other practices for subdividing the world have become more popular. There is a tendency today for teachers to divide the world into culture areas, each of which possesses distinctive characteristics related to world-wide developments and processes of change. The culture areas most commonly recognized are Europe, the Soviet Union, the Middle East, and North Africa, Africa south of the Sahara, the Orient (which is often itself subdivided into smaller cultural areas such as East-central Asia, Southeast Asia, and South Asia), the Pacific world, Latin America, and Anglo-America.

A scheme which is becoming even more common is to divide

the world into areas made up of communities of nations, that is, groups of nations characterized by common economic, social, and political ties. In the world as a whole, three major large communities of this kind can be recognized: the Atlantic Community, the Pacific Community, the Communist Community. Obviously, each of these three major communities may be further subdivided into smaller communities of nations.

In the study of these areas, whether defined as continents, culture areas, or national communities, questions are raised about (1) their location in the world, (2) the distribution of major natural and cultural phenomena within each, and (3) their roles in world affairs. In addition, emphasis is placed on the learners' development of selected work-study skills, such as map making. The problem-solving approach is emphasized, and a respect for the scientific method is inculcated.

By the time the child has completed the sixth or seventh grade, he has been introduced to most parts of the world and to the peoples and ways of living in these areas. The effectiveness of current programs, however, is open to question, for the conceptual framework which gives meaning to so many facts of significance in geography is generally not well developed. As a result much that is taught in the intermediate grades is not significant to many pupils, hence is not long remembered. The solution, many claim, is to increase the quantity and quality of geography teaching in our secondary schools and colleges. Let us turn our attention, then, to the role of geography in our high schools and institutions of higher learning.

In American High Schools

High school geography has reached its present form through a series of advances and retreats. Its content has ranged from the late-nineteenth-century emphasis on physical geography to the current focus on human, or culture, phenomena and regions.

Geography was introduced in American secondary schools toward the end of the eighteenth century as a study more practical for children of the middle classes than the classical education of colonial grammar schools. The progress of students, unfortunately, depended upon their ability to memorize answers to set questions concerning the location and character of places, and interest in the subject was never high.

About the middle of the nineteenth century, a course based on Fitch's *Outlines of Physical Geography* was introduced in a number of high schools. Instead of a study of countries, Fitch stressed the distribution of natural features from a world point of view. The appearance of such a course coincided with the widespread interest in science which had developed within secondary education during the latter half of the nineteenth century.

The study of physical geography was given an impetus in the 1890's by the publication of the "Report of the Committee of Ten of the National Education Association." This committee was headed by William Morris Davis, the acknowledged leader of geography in American universities during this period. As a result, physical geography became a laboratory science and was accepted as a college admission subject by the College Entrance Examination Board. The resulting courses emphasized man and his physical environment, not facts and mere descriptions.

Unfortunately, the study of physical geography proved in a few years to be a dull and uninteresting subject to most students, mainly because the courses were not well taught in the hands of unprepared teachers. It was not long, therefore, before other subjects, especially general science, were substituted for it. By 1910, the study of physical geography no longer played a dominant role in the high school curriculum.

In the meantime, a new trend developed. Interest began to grow in commercial and economic geography as national isolation declined. About the turn of the twentieth century, the United States began to look outward to distribute its growing surplus of goods and to invest its surplus capital. This brought about an interest in vocational education, high schools of commerce, and with them, the study of commercial geography. The popularity of commercial geography was to last for nearly forty years. Indeed, in 1929, Professor Rugg of Columbia University is reported to have said that at the senior high school level about the only kind of geography being taught was commercial geography and that in reality a great percentage of students electing commercial geography courses were those who were pursuing the vocational curriculum.

A third major trend began to set in during the early 1930's. There was a gradual lessening of interest in commercial geography, and many courses were absorbed into the fused social studies courses which had been developing at the high school level for more than a decade. At the same time, liberal arts colleges dropped geography as an accepted subject for college admission, and the last College Board Examination in the discipline was published. As William L. Mayo reports, "only the ghost of independent geography remained in the American high schools" in the 1930's.

But with the coming of World War II, geography experienced its first inkling of rebirth. The biggest impetus, however, to its development came during the late 1950's and early 1960's with modern advancements in science and technology, especially in Space Science. These developments have telescoped both time and space and have given new meaning to the term "one world." Today courses in world geography are more common in the ninth and tenth grades; and a High School Geography Project has been initiated by the Association of American Geographers with financial assistance from the Fund for the Advancement of Education and the National Science Foundation. Of no small importance is the fact that this project, designed to develop a variety of rigorous approaches to geography at the high school level, is being carried out by some of America's most eminent geographical scholars. Thus, interest in geography at the secondary school level, oriented in terms of world patterns of human, or cultural, phenomena, is again on the rise, and those involved with the high school project see geography at this level of instruction as part of the continuum of modern geographic education.

In Institutions of Higher Learning

Although geography is a very old field of study, it was not until 1903 that the first collegiate department was established in the United States. Prior to this development, which took place in the University of Chicago, various aspects of physical geography had been taught in Princeton and Harvard. Today more than thirty universities in all parts of the country offer the doctorate in the discipline.

In addition to work at the graduate level, most state colleges and universities, especially in the midwestern and far western states, offer undergraduate programs of study in the discipline. In recent years, the demand for more expert knowledge and understanding about the earth as the home of man has stimulated increased enrollments in these programs throughout the country. As a result, the Association of American Geographers, with the support of the National Science Foundation, has established a Commission of College Geography. The Commission has brought together panels of distinguished geographers to review specific problem areas in geographic education at the undergraduate level. Attention is being given by these panels to content and sequence of courses, interdisciplinary cooperation, the improvement of undergraduate teaching, and to techniques and methods of presentation of subject matter. In the six decades since 1903, the discipline of geography has become securely established as a subject of study in American institutions of higher learning. That it is not taught so widely in private institutions as in public-supported colleges and universities is a matter of considerable concern to geographers. A hoped-for remedy for this situation lies in the sustained and scientifically-grounded efforts that are under way to introduce current geographical research methods in college geography programs of study.

METHODS OF INSTRUCTION

The study of geography is often criticized in the United States as being dull and undiscriminating, with too much attention paid to the memorization of unrelated facts. As taught in many classrooms, there appears to be little structure to the discipline, no conceptual framework around which to orient one's knowledge or to give meaning to the facts being memorized, no specific mode of inquiry. Geography, when presented in this manner, becomes encyclopedic, and its pursuance defeats the production of skilled and informed young people capable of independent thought. Many examples can be cited to support such a contention. For example, one might consult any geography textbook at random. Count the number of cities "mentioned" and described without any apparent rhyme or reason. A multitude of facts is marshalled about each; but more often than not few of them are treated with meaning.

Geographers interested in the education of young people have fought against this practice for decades, beginning with the Committee of Ten in the 1890's. Even so, the discipline is not generally conceived by many who teach it in the elementary and secondary schools as a body of related facts, concepts, and theories.

Fortunately, there is a growing tendency, following the lead set by the physical and biological sciences, to help students think more theoretically about facts of significance to the geographer. More and more, students are being asked to work with raw data under the guidance of an expert teacher, to develop hypotheses about these data, and to search for supporting evidence of the hypothesis just as professional geographers do. Instead of being asked to memorize a body of information set forth in a textbook, pupils are being led to ask probing questions about the location and distribution of natural and man-made phenomena, and to seek answers to these questions, using their textbooks as a source of hypotheses, pertinent data, or supporting evidence. Eventually, this process should lead the students to discover the structure of the discipline that is inherent in the geographic mode of inquiry and in the major generalizations, laws, or theories which have been validated by the scholars in the field.

EDUCATIONAL MEDIA

To accomplish these goals requires a multitude of educational media—sound motion films, cartridges, filmstrips, study prints, slides, specimens, models, objects, transparent overlays for use with overhead projectors, charts and tables, readable maps and globes, better written and better illustrated textbooks, and more interesting supplementary reading materials. Of these, special attention is generally given to the use of maps and globes. These aids serve a variety of functions and are often considered to be the most important of the educational media available for use in the geography classroom. They are, at times, the best source of hypotheses concerning the distribution of phenomena over the earth's surface. They are also a source of data useful in testing geographical hypotheses. And, third, they are a means of expressing place relations of phenomena, and a help in demonstrating interactions between places. The use of maps in problem-solving situations depends, however, on the student's ability to read them effectively and efficiently. These abilities can be summarized as follows: to orient the map and to note directions; to grasp the scale of a map and to compute distances; to locate places on maps and globes by means of an established grid system; to note relative locations; to read and interpret the many symbols used on maps; and to compare distributions and make inferences about their place relationships. In order to develop these abilities, the study of geography commonly includes carefully designed and logically arranged map-reading and map-making experiences.

TEACHER PREPARATION

With the recent growth of interest in the United States in the study of geography at all levels of instruction, there is a serious shortage of teachers who understand and are able to transmit the structure of geographic knowledge and methods of inquiry to young people. Moreover, the situation is not likely to improve rapidly in the years ahead, for recent surveys show that only fifteen states and territories out of fifty-two require the completion of geography courses for the certification of elementary school teachers, and that only ten of the fifty-two states and territories certify secondary teachers with a separate certificate in the discipline. There are, moreover, a distressingly large number of states that will certify a teacher in geography on the basis of only four courses in the subject. From these statistics, it is readily apparent that many teachers in the United States are not adequately prepared in the discipline.

Based on its findings, a Committee of the National Council for Geographic Education, in 1964, drew up seventeen recommendations to improve the situation. It is too early to judge whether or not these recommendations will be accepted. In the meantime, much in-service work needs to be done to upgrade teachers who are assigned to instruct the youth of our nation about the world and its peoples. The amendment to the 1958 National Defense Education Act, passed in the fall of 1964, provides one means for accomplishing this objective through massive financial support for training teachers and for purchasing materials. An important start has already been made through this bill. The Higher Education Act of 1965 is another important teacher training vehicle, as is the pre-college education program of the National Science Foundation. While over the next four years as many as 8,000 teachers will probably receive sound and sophisticated training through such programs, they will remain a mere handful compared to the large number who are not prepared to teach the discipline effectively, but who are, nonetheless, attempting to do so.

CONCLUSIONS

In the light of these remarks, it is not possible to conclude that geography as yet plays an outstanding role in American education. However, the immediate future is a brighter one for the discipline. More and more students in American colleges and universities are finding geography courses challenging and meaningful; courses in world geography are multiplying rapidly in the secondary schools; and more attention is being given to the discipline of geography in elementary school programs of learning. Methods of instruction are becoming more problem-oriented, new educational media are being created, and ways and means of upgrading the classroom teacher are being sought. Thus, at this critical time in the history of the United States, when an understanding of the world and its peoples is becoming so necessary, geography is beginning to play a more and more significant role in the American educational system. The lessons to be learned from this process, in the light of changing geographic educational trends outside of the United States, can be of considerable value to the world community of geographers and educators. To this end, a task for all geographers throughout the world is to seek out and exploit promising avenues of international communication that will enable the world community of scholars to grapple more effectively with geography in systems of education.

SUGGESTED READINGS

Brigham, A. P., and Dodge, R. E., "Nineteenth Century Textbooks of Geography." In *The Thirty-second Yearbook of the National Society for the Study of Education.* Bloomington, Ill.: Public School Publishing Company, 1933.

Davis, W. M., "The Progress of Geography in the Schools." In *Geographical Essays.* New York: Dover, 1954.

Freeman, T. W., *A Hundred Years of Geography.* Chicago: Aldine Publishing Company, 1961.

Gopsill, G. H., *The Teaching of Geography.* London: Macmillan and Company, 1958.

Mayo, W. L., *The Development and Status of Secondary School Geography in the United States and Canada.* Ann Arbor Mich.: University Publishers, 1965.

Mayo, W. L., *Geography in the High School.* Bloomington, Ill.: McKnight and McKnight, 1949.

Taylor, G. R. (ed.), *Geography in the Twentieth Century.* New York: Philosophical Library, 1951.

Wright, J. K., *Geography in the Making.* New York: The American Geographical Society, 1952.

18 GEOGRAPHY AND SYSTEMS THEORY

John R. Borchert

Recent years have seen the development of a body of theory and method for general systems analysis. The purpose is to better understand the workings of large groups of regularly interacting and interdependent items, termed "systems." This development has accompanied the elaboration of linear programming and rapid increase in the capacity of electronic computers. Many kinds of systems, and their functions, can be simulated in compact form and at great speed by modern computers. For the computer, itself, is a system.

Application of systems analysis has increased man's ability to follow and control a variety of dynamic organizational features in both nature and society—fiscal budgets, wholesale distribution, manufacturing processes, floodwaters, traffic snarls, and many more. Scientists from a variety of disciplines have studied and helped to describe the general characteristics of systems. Important concepts, in addition to "system," itself, include "structures" and "flows," "open" and "closed" systems, and the "steady state" of a system.

The general concept and its component parts are of importance to the science of geography, and it is worthwhile to explore both the reasons why this is so and some recent developments in American geography which reflect the influence of general systems theory.

The term "system" has been used traditionally to describe certain features of great geographical importance. River systems and transportation systems are common examples.

In both of these cases the "system" implies not only a set of static lines—a structure—on the map, but also a flow of people or material from initial locations to new locations. These locational changes, in turn, alter the structure. For example, the flow of a stream system is accompanied by erosion and deposition of sediment. Hence the flow alters the structure as hills are lowered, gullies wear headward, canyons are carved, or meanders migrate on the floodplain. Likewise, the flow of people in a transportation system generally results in either temporary or long-term shifts in the distribution of population. Hence the pattern of settlement is changed by the flow. The flow of goods and raw materials in a transportation system results in long-term alterations in the geographic distribution of resources. Again, flow alters structure.

But the flows in a river or transportation system change endlessly in response to other changes initiated outside the system. For instance, a storm entering and passing across the river basin may produce a temporary twenty-fold increase in the volume of water flowing through the system. A drought may cut the flow by 95 per cent. Changes in the rate of erosion and deposition—that is, the rate of transformation of the structure of the system—accompany these externally induced changes in flow. The flow and rate of structural change in the transportation system may be similarly altered. Numerous examples come to mind—economic booms or depressions, technologic innovations, new styles, new laws—all of which might characterize a society or a region transcending the particular system. Thus the river system or the transportation system is an "open" system in the sense that the input to it and the output from it are altered by external conditions. The changes one observes within each system cannot be entirely explained by the components of the system itself.

There is an average flow of water at any point in the river

system, and an average flow of traffic at any point in the transportation system. For example, an average annual rainfall is distributed geographically over the drainage basin of the Mississippi river system. It yields an average annual runoff, an average annual stream flow, and an average annual discharge of water and mud into the Gulf of Mexico. This whole set of inputs, flows, and yields might be described as the "steady state" of the Mississippi system during the period of historical record for which the averages have been computed. A certain average input of water produces a given output and a given rate of change in the structure. But, of course, the average occurs only a small fraction of the time. There is a whole range of conditions between extreme flood and extreme drought. Any of these conditions has a certain probability of occurrence. Furthermore, the averages and extremes observed in the period of historical record have occurred within a still wider range of unobserved extremes which occur over much longer periods of time. The longer-term, wider swings are suggested, for example, by the reconstructed climates of the Pleistocene glacial epochs and their impacts upon the flow and structure of the Mississippi drainage system.

It is not difficult to think of other systems with extremely important geographic dimensions. The world wind system, or general circulation of the atmosphere, is one. There are the great centers of action—the semi-permanent anticyclones and cyclones. These are centers of divergence and convergence within a vast system of flows. External environmental conditions put heat and moisture into the system. The flows redistribute these properties over the face of the earth, impart distinctive climatic characteristics to large regions, and generate boundaries at the edges of those regions, where unlike airstreams converge or new sets of external factors are introduced. The whole system is constantly adjusting and readjusting to changes in its environment. These changes result in part from flows within the system itself, and in part from changes in external factors such as the amount of heat stored in the oceans or the angle of inclination of the earth's axis. The world wind and pressure maps of our atlases depict the average or the hypothetical steady state of the system. Many other maps are needed to show variant patterns that may occur with different degrees of probability.

Or take the circulation system which radiates from the oil and gas fields of the western Gulf Coast of the southern United States. One can conceive the producing region as a center of action, with its distinctive facilities and output generating a flow of mineral fuel into a vast network of land and water transportation routes. At points lying along those routes the oil and gas are transformed into other useful compounds, electricity, and useless waste materials. Output from the system generates regional concentrations of industry and air pollution on the southern shores of Lake Michigan, the Delaware estuary, and in northeastern New Jersey. It helps to generate the flow of traffic on road, rail, and airline which converges on cities over most of the United States.

The system is open. It responds to numerous changes in its external environment. The flow of oil and gas from the producing region rises or falls in response to production investment decisions made in New York or Pittsburgh, regulations promulgated in Washington or Austin or Baton Rouge, strategic military decisions made in Moscow, or changes in consumer demand in the region of a winter cold wave in the Middle West. It is linked to other systems—to the traffic flow system at thousands of retail distribution points, to the atmospheric circulation at the mouths of smokestacks of the great refining centers. It is part of a larger system of oil and gas production, conversion, and distribution which includes similar geographic structures and flows throughout the world.

Metropolitan population, agricultural production and processing, administrative centers and linkages in a national state, and most other topics of geographic study can be conceived as systems. These systems are open. They exist at many different scales. They are interrelated and overlapping. And usually they can be considered as subsystems of some larger, more nearly transcendental system. In fact, to say that "subsystems" exist within larger systems is often simply another way to put the traditional problems of defining levels in a hierarchy of regions or places, or selecting the area and scale of generalization for studying a geographical topic.

In a number of ways, systems theory restates organizing concepts which are traditional in geography. But it also makes some valuable new contributions. It emphasizes the dynamic nature of some features which geography has usually considered in static terms, or the variability of systems which have been considered traditionally in "steady state" terms. It requires more rigorous descriptive statements, and places more emphasis on the need for precise and comparable observations. It emphasizes interaction and interrelationships. To some extent, it provides a common language with other sciences and also helps to dissolve the dichotomy between "physical" and "cultural" elements of geography. And it helps to adapt the enormous new power of electronic computers to the problems of geographic description and analysis.

In short, it is clear that the development of general systems theory, at the geographic scale, is directly applicable to geographic science. It seeks to illuminate the basic intellectual problem which has motivated geographic study—the need to see one's self in perspective within the changing patterns of man's resources and activities on the face of the earth. Furthermore, within the "systems" concept one finds parallels to the long-time geographic concepts of gradients, flows, hierarchies, networks, regions, boundaries, historical geography (time series), and the more recent notions of geographic prediction. One also finds the idea, implicit in much geographic research, that the study of changing form and pattern in a dynamic system is, in itself, a method of basic scientific analysis. Clearly geographers have been performing some kinds of systems analysis and have made their own contribution to its development.

The relationship between geography and general systems theory has been developed thus far most extensively by an *ad hoc* Committee on Geography in the National Academy of Sciences–National Research Council. Seven distinguished American geographers comprised the committee, which was appointed in 1963. Its report, published in 1965, is entitled *The Science of Geography*. The committee's task was to examine new and promising research methods for geography, to identify geographical topics that require greater attention and development, and to evaluate geography's potential contribution to the general progress of science.

The committee considered the overriding problem of geography to be the understanding of the "vast system on the earth comprising man and the natural environment." To be sure, geography merely shares this problem with other branches of science. An intensified attack upon the problem becomes increasingly urgent, the committee pointed out, as the earth's population multiplies, pressure on resources grows even faster, and systems of transportation and communications make the parts of the world increasingly interrelated.

The committee focused its report on four fields within geography which it considered to be the most promising places to concentrate time and effort in the immediate future. These four "growing edges" of the field include physical, cultural, and political geography, and location theory. The committee placed strong emphasis on the adoption of systems concepts and analytical methods. Some of the suggested major research opportunities reflect that emphasis: "Further observation of physiographic processes in a systems context" (physical geography); "study of the nature and rate of diffusion of culture elements" (cultural geography); "interfaces of national political systems," "internal spatial organization of the giant state" (political geography); "flow linkages between places," "temporal dynamics of spatial structure and spatial systems" (location theory). In effect, the committee identified four major subsystems of the transcendant Man-Natural Environment system and emphasized opportunities, which it perceived, for rewarding studies of those subsystems. Throughout its report, the committee focused attention on the interests and competencies within the geographic profession that "cooperatively, with other branches of science, can contribute to interdisciplinary progress in understanding man and his environment."

The National Academy of Sciences–National Research Council committee went on to make a series of recommendations for action, based on its study. It urged increased support of research on the "growing edges" of geography generally. In particular, it recommended support of dual doctoral degrees in geography and related sciences concerned with the Man-Natural Environment system, increased numbers of pre-doctoral fellowships for both resident and field study, support of advanced study institutes in physical and political geography, support of several data centers specifically to help advance the effectiveness of new computing systems for geographic purposes, and establishment of a high-level, interdisciplinary committee on the Man-Natural Environment system by the National Academy of Sciences.

There has been some concern within the American geographic profession regarding both the findings and the recommendations of this *ad hoc* committee. Some consider the findings to have placed too much emphasis upon certain parts of the total effort of American geography—those parts which could be put most readily in the language of modern systems analysis. Furthermore, it has been argued, this imbalance will be magnified and built into the field permanently by emphasizing unduly those same components of the field in the expanded training programs and advanced institutes which the committee advocates.

Others within American geography have taken a different position. They have argued that the translation of many traditional concepts of geography into modern systems terminology may be helpful in promoting the necessary dialogue between geography and other branches of science concerned with the same overriding problem. They have argued further that the successful establishment of all the expanded and new programs advocated by the committee, and operation of those programs over the next decade, cannot change the direction of the field in any revolutionary way; for the field is growing so rapidly that even the committee's ambitious program will involve only a very small fraction of the population of professional and practicing geographers. There will continue to be strong and growing needs for manpower and widespread sources of support all across the geographic profession.

On balance, it appears that modern systems theory has brought to geography a new language and some new tools. These are important partly because of the contemporaneous development of new computers and data systems. But they are also important because of the new needs and opportunities for interaction between geographers and a growing number of other scientists concerned with the transcendent Man-Environment system. Insofar as the new tools are used by geographers, they may well implement geography's traditional quest for empirical knowledge about the world and its places. They may also help geographers to perform a traditional function of geography—to bridge between the "social" and "natural" sciences. And introduction of systems analysis hardly further complicates, and might simplify, an already great need to train many more professional geographers efficiently and rigorously and to help to educate broadly not only many more professional geographers, but also millions of other Americans.

SUGGESTED READINGS

Ackerman, E. A. (ed.), *The Science of Geography*. Washington, D.C.: National Academy of Sciences–National Research Council, 1965.
Ackerman, E. A., Borchert, J. R., and James, P. E., "The President's Session, Report, *ad hoc* Committee on Geography, National Acad-

emy of Sciences–National Research Council on the Science of Geography." *The Professional Geographer*, XVII (July 1965), 30–37.

Chorley, R. J., *Geomorphology and General Systems Theory*. Professional Paper 500-B. Washington, D.C.: U. S. Geological Survey, 1962.

19 GEOGRAPHY'S SUBFIELDS AND ITS UNITY

George Kish

Geography is as old as man's first search for a bit of soil to scratch for plantings, for a path that leads to water, for a trail to a place where hard rock for arrowheads may be found. Geography is as new as man's current search to relieve urban congestion, to establish well-marked international boundaries, to describe and analyze vegetation patterns in remote parts of the earth.

If, in Pope's words, "the proper study of mankind is man," then geography defines its task as the study of man in his habitat, the earth. Geography deals with two types of phenomena, those established as part of our natural environment and those that have come about as a result of the interaction of man and nature. In the study of the first of these two types, geography is bent upon understanding and describing the hard crust of the earth, the lithosphere; the liquid matter that covers the greater part of the earth, the hydrosphere; and the earth's gaseous envelope, the atmosphere. As a result of man's interaction with his environment, the *noosphere* has come into existence. This is man's dwelling place, where he has, since he first separated from his primate ancestors, consciously and continuously attempted to transform nature.

Even this most generalized view reveals a duality that, in a very real sense, has been part of geography since its first practitioners, the Greeks, took a long and searching look at their environment.

Geography is concerned with the stage where the drama of human life takes place, with the physical properties of man's environment. It is equally concerned with man's activities on this stage—his actions in shaping the natural environment. But this duality is more apparent than real, for in geography man and his environment are truly inseparable. It is not only that his actions, from birth to death, take place within it; more importantly, from the beginnings of civilization man has shaped nature, and nature has influenced the actions of man. Man has cut forests and tilled the soil, exposing it thereby to erosion and radically changing its texture, complexion, depth, and composition; man has dammed rivers and changed their regime; man has, of late, poured vast quantities of carbon and carbon residue into the air, thereby inducing significant changes in the climates of cities. Similarly, nature has, quite effectively so far, limited man's utilization of deserts, both of cold and drought; it has compelled man, through the presence of epidemic and epizootic agents and vectors, to shun substantial portions of the earth as settlement areas; it has made man's life insecure through irregularly recurring atmospheric disturbances, hurricanes and typhoons, that so far have escaped even man's attempts to forecast, much less to prevent them.

Man and nature are inseparable, and in the same manner geography cannot be separated into two distinct branches, one devoted to the study of natural, and the other to the study of human, phenomena on earth. If physical geography is "a satisfaction of man's curiosity as to how the natural world is organized . . . on the earth's surface," human geography is man's attempt to organize in an orderly system his understanding of the manner in which society has established patterns of settlement, of land use, of transportation, of sovereign states, on the face of the earth.

Geography deals with phenomena of nature and of society on earth, the dwelling place of man. This dual focus of its interests has given rise, in the past hundred years, to the gradual emergence of many subfields, each with its emphasis on one specific aspect of geography, yet each connected with the others because of its interest in man-earth relationships.

The tools of geography in accomplishing its aims are the written word, the picture, and the map. Generalizations derived from many individual observations provide the basis for written statements, descriptive and analytical. Pictures drawn and painted, or produced through the eye of the camera, can convey shape and position and dimensions, but they are limited in scope to what the human eye or the camera can take in at one time.

The oldest and best tool of the geographer is the map. Maps, by use of a grid showing meridians (lines of longitude) and parallels (lines of latitude), can define with great accuracy the position of a phenomenon, or of a group of phenomena, on earth. Maps can show, by the use of colors, or of shading, the location of a place, or a district, and whether it is on a mountain or in a wide, flat plain. Maps show at a glance such important characteristics as the location of places with relation to rivers and lakes, and indicate whether places are on the ocean or on an inland sea. Maps are the geographer's ideal tool to show what he is most concerned with: the distribution of natural and cultural phenomena on the face of the earth.

As long as man has been interested in his surroundings, he has drawn maps. Across the ages, maps have rendered faithfully the state of a given civilization's knowledge of the world: ancient maps of China invariably show it as the center of the universe. Maps have reflected religious belief and dogma: thus medieval maps show the earth as a flat disc and place Paradise at its eastern extremity. Maps suffer from the secrecy surrounding valuable discoveries of hitherto unknown places: during the Age of Discovery, Portugal forbade the selling of maps showing Portuguese conquests and sailing routes to any foreigner, under pain of death. Today our maps are still a mirror of our age: they display our knowledge of earth processes, restrict the information they show to what governments see fit to reveal, yet remain the unsurpassed means of presenting, through a universally accepted symbolism, the findings of modern geography.

To know our earth, geography, physical geography, concerns itself with features that characterize its surface, with the soils that are derived from that surface, with the climate that regulates the life cycle of plants, with sweet and salt water on land and in the seas, and with the carpet of vegetation that covers earth features over large areas.

The study of the surface of the earth is geomorphology, a study of shape and form and process. Its subject is the grade of slopes that regulate the downward movement of water, the runoff. It studies the ways in which wind and running water and temperature changes work together, determine the shape of a valley, round out the outline of a mountain and, over long periods of time, succeed in transforming an entire landscape. This process, the erosion cycle, creates low plains where mountains once had been, deepens and widens river valleys, and replaces sharp and well-defined mountain crests with smooth, well-worn forms.

The study of surface features is an indispensable introduction to soils, which are the product of a long and intricate formative process. The texture of soils, their depth, their composition, and their use to man are determined by other inorganic and organic factors. Bedrock serves as the parent material of soils; weathering, the action of wind and water and temperature changes, influences its structure; organic, plant and animal, matter added to it determines its usefulness to man. Modern soil science, the analysis and classification of the world's soils into a few large categories, was the work of Russian and American scientists. On the basis of their studies, soils are now mapped according to their composition and classified according to their fertility. Soil conservation helps retain soils, by protecting them from soil erosion by wind and water, through such techniques as contour plowing and the planting of protective vegetation cover.

Rain and snow fall on the land, winds sweep across it, and sun shines on it. The yearly cycle of the weather, as ancient a force in the life of man as his collective memory, shapes his daily life and governs his use of the land. Man is still almost completely dependent on the weather, and is therefore interested in knowing about it, in long-range studies of its characteristics. Climate is the average of weather conditions based on observations of many decades: conditions of precipitation, winds, temperature, sunshine, and cloud cover are the raw material of climatology.

Observing weather phenomena, climatology helps farmers by furnishing them with descriptions of climate in small, well-defined areas that may enable them to undertake ventures involving special crops and demanding special climatic conditions. Climatology has also established general classification schemes of climatic types, dividing the world into major regions of more or less uniform climates and thus provides valuable generalizations about the earth.

Water, usable, sweet drinking water, indispensable for the survival of man, beast, or plant, is a finite substance on earth. Climatology can predict the yearly amount of precipitation and its seasonal distribution, but it is hydrology that concerns itself with the fate that befalls water. Hydrology surveys the available water reserves on the surface and below it. It studies the regime of rivers, their yearly change from high to low water, forecasts floods, and makes flood control possible.

Contrasted with our supply of sweet, unpolluted water that is rapidly shrinking with the growth of population and the continuous increase in industrial and domestic waste substances dumped into our rivers and lakes, the world ocean presents a virtually unlimited source of water. But this is saline water, and until desalinization is accomplished the oceans in this respect remain a useless substance, a wasteland, to man.

Oceanography concerns itself not so much with the transformation of salt into sweet water, a problem of technology, as with the study of the physical and biological characteristics of the world oceans. It is the latter of these that is of the greatest interest to geography—which might well be defined as the study of man's place on earth and his search of usable resources. As a source of both plant foods and animal proteins, the oceans may well become within the foreseeable future the greatest remaining reservoir of life-sustaining substances. At the same time, submarine studies are likely to reveal vast deposits of fuels, metals, and minerals at the bottom of the sea, resources that represent an immense potential addition to man's resource base.

Natural vegetation offers the best indicator of the combined effect of surface features, soils, and climate on the appearance on the landscape, just as present-day vegetation in many areas reflects the impact of man on nature and the extent of the resulting change. Phytogeography, or plant geography, the study of vegetation types, is in this sense the keystone of physical geography. Since the landscape in its totality is accessible to any careful observer, the classification established by plant geography has long ago become part of our everyday speech. Thus we speak of the prairies of the American Middle West or of the humid pampas of Argentina, of the hardwood forests of the eastern United States or of Central Europe, of the dry grasslands of Kansas or of the steppes of south European Russia. Implicit in our terms and clearly defined by plant geography is the impact of man and the cultural change he has irrevocably introduced in the natural landscape.

Though the majority of geographical studies concern themselves with the present, there has long been a strong interest among geographers in the reconstruction of past landscapes and of man's use of, and adjustment to, these landscapes in earlier historical times. Historical geography thus defined establishes a bridge between the two main divisions of geography: physical geography, the study of our terrestrial, natural environment, and cultural geography, the study of the mutual impact of man and his environment.

278

In physical geography the focus is on nature, in cultural geography the focus shifts to man. Cultural geography is the study of the forms of man's dwelling places, of his use and misuse of the environment, of his pursuits to earn a living, of his problems in managing the urban setting of human life, of the spatial problems posed by political conflict.

Settlement geography is the study of the forms of human settlement. It concerns itself with individual dwellings, for they often reveal cultural tradition and technique, and the nature of the local environment. Thus mud-brick constructions seem to be common to many desert areas, while the use of steel-enforced concrete is limited to advanced industrial and urbanized societies, while the presence of window screens indicates a strong desire to keep insects away from man's eating and sleeping quarters. Settlement geography is equally interested in the morphology of groups of dwellings, whether they are of the nucleated, village type so widespread in the Old World, or conform to the dispersed type, composed of individual, widely spaced homes characteristic of recent settlements of European origin in the Americas and in Australia.

Man's use and misuse of his environment and his pursuits to earn a living form the subject matter of a cluster of special fields of geography, economic geography. Agricultural geography is concerned with primary production on land, with food and feed and fibers, whether they are part of a self-sufficient, subsistence-oriented farm economy or of market-oriented, large-scale farming enterprises.

Another branch of economic geography deals with the distribution of the fuels, metals, and minerals that represent the mining aspect of primary production. The geography of manufacturing has a more complex field of study, the secondary production of machinery and consumer goods, and the factors that govern the concentration of industry in our world. These are studies of location, of the influences that shaped the rise of the great industrial centers of our earth: readily available fuels and raw materials, good transportation systems, skilled manpower.

In all aspects of economic geography, descriptive studies are giving way to planning studies and to application potential. Man is gradually recognizing that the resources upon which industrial growth depends are both limited and scattered widely on earth, but he is also aware that growth of industry has become the symbol of progress and well-being for all societies. The part played by geography and geographers in planning includes forecasts of the availability of food, feed, and fibers for men and animals and industrial needs; of the location of new industrial regions and the creation of transportation systems to serve them; of the problems created by the growth of cities.

This brief survey of the fields of interest grouped together under the name of cultural geography assumes that intercourse among human beings takes place in an atmosphere of mutual understanding. This has not often been the case: conflict rather than concord characterizes most of our history. Since conflict is and always has been such an important facet of relations among human beings, the interaction between the setting of conflict and the agents of conflict, the geography of politics has played an important part in geography since its earliest beginnings.

The study of frontiers; of the elements of power: raw materials, sources of energy, means of transport, trained manpower; the expansion and concentration of the political state in relation to its position in space and to its territory and population; these are some of the main themes of the geography of politics or political geography. To these in recent years there has been added a growing interest in the spatial distribution of voting, the one variable in internal political life that allows accurate measurement and yields some interesting facts on the political process.

It is the study of the distribution of men on our earth, population geography, that occupies the key position in cultural geography. Maps showing the distribution and density of people in a given area—the size and direction of internal and international migrations; the rates of growth, of birth, of death; the incidence of disease—sum up the findings of settlement, agricultural, manufacturing, and political studies in geography. In an age of rapidly expanding population, the danger spots on earth, the areas of maximum growth, appear clearly marked on a map of demographic trends.

When looked on in its original Greek context, "geography" may be interpreted as a description of the earth; one of this science's main purposes is to provide a meaningful and satisfactory explanation of the distribution of mankind on earth. The map of population distribution, in this context, represents the starting point of geographical study: Why are there people living in that particular place? What are the natural conditions prevailing there? How and to what extent have people succeeded in changing the natural environment? What contributions did the environment make to their success or failure in establishing themselves in that particular part of the earth?

These questions partake of both physical and cultural geography. They indicate geography's concern both with natural and with cultural factors. They underline the interdependence of terrestrial phenomena and act as guideposts to the future of geography, the study of man in his earthly environment.

SUGGESTED READINGS

Ackerman, E. A., *Geography as a Fundamental Research Discipline,* Research Paper No. 53. Chicago: University of Chicago Press, 1958.
Ackerman, E. A. (ed.), *The Science of Geography.* Washington, D.C.: National Academy of Sciences–National Research Council, 1965.
Hartshorne, R., "The Nature of Geography." *Annals of the Association of American Geographers,* XXIX (1939), 1–482.

Whittlesey, D., "The Horizon of Geography." *Annals of the Association of American Geographers,* XXV (1945), 1–36.

Wright, J. K., "Terrae Incognitae: The Place of Imagination in Geography." *Annals of the Association of American Geographers,* XXXVII (1947), 1–15.

Index

peasantry of, 202; spatial organization of manufacturing in, 27

Fairbanks, Alaska, 230
family, head of, 96–97; non-urban, low-income, 105; of roving poor, 98–99; urban, 101
family income, U. S., 94–95, 108
farm family, income and status of, 96–98
farm land, abandonment of, 65–66; value of, 70
farm prices, decline of, 89
farms and farming, classification of, 213–214; cotton, 72; dairy, 86–88; gentleman, 73; Great Plains, 78; land element in, 210–213; Midwest, 75–91; migrant labor in, 98–100; Mountain West, 78; Pacific Coast, 78; "part-owner" system, 70; peasant, *see* peasant farms and farming; "sidewalk," 71; technology and, 214
feed lots, 85
fertilizers, chemical, 182
Finland, continuous settlement area in, 225; "Norden" area and, 222; settlement experience of, 233
fisheries, resources of, 122
fisheries commissions, international, 119
fishing and fishing industry, 118–120; Canadian and Japanese along U. S. coast, 119; on foreign coasts, 119; future of, 120; Russian fishing in American waters, 119
Florida, bulk transportation connection in, 17; citrus industry, 67–68; coastal waters of, 117, 122; continental shelf along, 116–117; migrants in, 99; orange crop, 20; petroleum exploratory work, 120; poultry production, 68–69; sulfur

from coastal waters, 120; titanium sands off coast of, 122
Florida Keys, offshore islands, 114
Food Costs (bulletin), 88 n.
forage, 86
forests, 278
"Four Seas," of United States, 153
France, North Africa and, 164
free world, settlement of higher latitudes of, 222
fringe settlement zones, 223–231
fruit-growing, transportation and, 20
Fuchs, Victor R., 93, 94 n.
Fund for the Advancement of Education, 257

Garrison, William L., 13
Gaulle, Charles de, 148
General Geography (Varenius), 6
Geneva Conference on the Law of the Sea, 117
geographical analog, 131, 141
"Geographical and Geological Survey of the Rocky Mountain Region" (Powell), 7
geographical prediction, 124–125, 131, 144
geographical knowledge, peasant farming and, 209–219
"geographical location theory," 12–13, 26–27, 31–32, 269
geographic thought, continuity and change in, 3–14; recent stages in, 124–125
geography, agricultural, 279; in American education, 251–263; application and prediction in, 127; college programs of, 258–259; commercial, 256–257; cultural, *see* cultural geography; duality of, 273–275; economic, 256–257, 279–280; economic development and, 174–186; education and, 251–263; in elementary schools, 253–255; evolution of, 6–8;